PBY - Top Rated Rocky Mountain Adventures

Picked-By-You Guides®
Top Rated Outdoor Series

# Top Rated™
# Rocky Mountain Adventures

Includes: Colorado, Idaho, Montana, New Mexico, Utah,
Wyoming, Alberta, British Columbia, Saskatchewan
and Yukon Territories

by Maurizio Valerio

# PICKED-BY-YOU GUIDES®

Top Rated Outdoor Series

Copies of this book can be ordered from:

**Picked-By-You**

PO Box 718

Baker City, OR 97814

Phone: (800) 279-0479 • Fax: (541) 523-5028

www.topguides.com • e-mail: maurice@topguides.com

Artwork by Steamroller Studios, Cover Art by Fifth Street Design
Maps by Map Art, Cartesia Software
Printed in Korea

Publisher's Cataloging-in-Publication
*(Provided by Quality Books, Inc.)*

Valerio, Maurice.
   Top rated Rocky Mountain adventures : includes: Colorado, Idaho, Montana, New Mexico, Utah, Wyoming, Alberta, British Columbia, Saskatchewan and Yukon Territories / by Maurizio Valerio. -- 1st ed.
      p. cm. -- (Top rated outdoor series)
      Includes indexes.
      Preassigned LCCN: 98-68000
      ISBN: 1-889807-16-8

   1. Outdoor recreation--Rocky Mountains (Region)--Directories.   2. Rocky Mountains (Region)--Guidebooks
   I. Title.

GV191.42.R63 V35 1999            796.5 02578
                                 QBI98-1377

To Allison, Marco and Nini

## About the Author

Maurizio (Maurice) Valerio received a Doctoral degree Summa cum Laude in Natural Science, majoring in Animal Behaviour, from the University of Parma (Italy) in 1981, and a Master of Arts degree in Zoology from the University of California, Berkeley in 1984.

He is a rancher, a writer and a devoted outdoorsman who decided to live with the wild animals that he cherishes so much in the Wallowa Mountains of Northeast Oregon. He has traveled extensively in the Old and New World, for more than 25 years. He is dedicated to preserving everyone's individual right of a respectful, knowledgeable and diversified use of our Outdoor Resources.

# Table of Contents

# Acknowledgments

It is customary in this section to give credit to those who have contributed to the realization of the end product. The Picked-By-You Guides® started three years ago as a little personal crusade and has evolved into a totally challenging, stimulating and rewarding full time commitment.

My deep thanks must go first to all the Captains, Ranchers, Guides, Lodges and Outfitters who decided to trust our honesty and integrity. They have taken a leap of faith in sharing their lists of clients with us and for this we are truly honored and thankful.

They have constantly encouraged our idea. Captains have taught us the difference between skinny fishing and skinny dipping, while River Guides have patiently help us to identify rafters, purlins, catarafts and J-rig rafts. They were also ready to give us a badly needed push forward every time this very time-consuming idea came to a stall. We have come to know many of them through pleasant phone chats, e-mails, faxes and letters. They now sound like old friends on the phone and we are certain we all share a deep respect for the mountains, the deserts and the waters of this great country of ours.

The Picked-By-You Team (both in the office and abroad), with months of hard work, skills, ingenuity, good sense of humor and pride, have then transformed a simple good idea into something a bit more tangible and much more exciting. They all have put their hearts in the concept and their hands and feet in the dirt. Some with a full-time schedule, some with a part-time collaboration, all of them bring their unique and invaluable style and contribution.

My true thanks to Brent Beck, Lindsay Benson, Bob Erdmann, Robert Evans, Cheryl Fisher, Brian Florence, Sally Georgeson, Grace Martin, Kevin McNamara, Jerry Meek, Allison C. Mickens, Tom Novak, Shelby Sherrod, Dyanne Van Swoll, Giuseppe Verdi and Mr. Peet's Coffee and Tea.

Last, but not least, my sincere, profound, and loving gratitude to my wife Allison. Her patient support, her understanding, her help and her skills have been the fuel which started and stoked this fire. Her laughter has been the wind to fan it.

To you Allie, with a toast to the next project...just kidding!

Maurizio (Maurice) Valerio

# Preface

The value of information depends on its usefulness. Simply put, whatever allows you to make informed choices will be to your advantage. To that end, Picked-By-You Guides® aims to take the guesswork out of selecting services for outdoor activities. Did you get what you paid for? From Picked-By-You Guides®' point of view, the most reliable indicator is customer satisfaction.

The information in this book is as reliable as those who chose to participate. In the process of selecting the top professionals, Picked-By-You Guides® contacted all licensed guides, outfitters and businesses which provide services for outdoor activities. They sought to include everyone but not all who were contacted agreed to participate according to the rules. Thus, the omission of a guide, outfitter or service does not automatically mean they didn't qualify based on customer dissatisfaction.

The market abounds with guidebooks by 'experts' who rate a wide range of services based on their personal preferences. The value of the Picked-By-You concept is that businesses earn a place in these books only when they receive favorable ratings from a majority of clients. If ninety percent of the customers agree that their purchase of services met or exceeded their expectations, then it's realistic to assume that you will also be satisfied when you purchase services from the outdoor professionals and businesses included in this book.

It's a fact of life; not everyone is satisfied all of the time or by the same thing. Individual experiences are highly subjective and are quite often based on expectations. One person's favorable response to a situation might provoke the opposite reaction in another. A novice might be open to any experience without any preconceived notions while a veteran will be disappointed when anything less than great expectations aren't met.

If you select any of the businesses in this book, chances are excellent that you will know what you are buying. A diversity of clients endorsed them because they believed the services they received met or exceeded their expectations. Picked-By-You Guides® regards that information more valuable than a single observer or expert's point of view.

The intent behind Picked-By-You Guides® is to protect the consumer from being misled or deceived. It is obvious that these clients were given accurate information which resulted in a positive experience and a top rating.

The number of questionnaire responses which included detailed and sometimes lengthy comments impressed upon us the degree to which people value their experiences. Many regard them as "once-in-a-lifetime" and "priceless," and they heaped generous praise on those whose services made it possible.

Picked-By-You Guides® has quantified the value of customer satisfaction and created a greater awareness of top-rated outdoor professionals. It remains up to you to choose and be the judge of your own experience. With the help of this book, you will have the advantage of being better informed when making that pick.

Robert Evans, *information specialist*

# The Picked-By-You Guides® Idea

## Mission Statement

The intent of this publication is to provide the outdoor enthusiast and his/her family with an objective and easy-to-read reference source that would list only those businesses and outdoor professionals who have **agreed to be rated** and have been overwhelmingly endorsed by their past clients.

There are many great outdoor professionals (Guides, Captains, Ranches, Lodges, Outfitters) who deserve full recognition for putting their experience, knowledge, long hours, and big heart, into this difficult job. With this book we want to reward those deserving professionals while providing an invaluable tool to the general public.

Picked-By-You Guides® are the only consumer guides to outdoor activities.

In this respect it would be useful to share the philosophy of our Company succinctly illustrated by our Mission Statement:

> "To encourage and promote the highest professional and ethical standards among those individuals, Companies, Groups or Organizations who provide services to the Outdoor Community.

To communicate and share the findings and values of our research and surveys to the public and other key groups.

To preserve everyone's individual right of a respectful, knowledgeable and diversified use of our Outdoor Resources".

Our business niche is well defined and our job is simply to listen carefully.

## THEY 'the experts' Vs. WE 'the People'

Picked-By-You books were researched and compiled by **asking people such as yourself**, who rafted, fished, hunted or rode a horse on a pack trip with a particular outdoor professional or business, to rate their services, knowledge, skills and performance.

*Only the ones who received A- to A+ scores from their clients are found listed in these pages.*

The market is flooded with various publications written by 'experts' claiming to be the ultimate source of information for your vacation. We read books with titles such as " The Greatest River Guides", "The Complete Guide to the Greatest Fishing Lodges" etc.

We do not claim to be experts in any given field, but we rather pass to history as good....listeners. In the preparation of the Questionnaires we listened first to the outdoor professionals' point of view and then to the comments and opinions of thousands of outdoor enthusiasts. We then organized the findings of our research and surveys in this and other publications of this series.

Thus we will not attempt to tell how to fish, how to paddle or what to bring on your trip. We are leaving this to the outdoor professionals featured in this book, for they have proven to be outstanding in providing much valuable information before, during and after your trip.

## True [paid] advertising: an oxymoron

Chili with beans is considered a redundant statement for the overwhelming majority of cooks but it is an insulting oxymoron for any native Texan.

In the same way while 'true paid advertising' is a correct statement for some, it is a clear contradiction in terms for us and certainly many of you. A classic oxymoron.

This is why we do not accept commissions, donations, invitations, or, as many publishers cleverly express it, "...extra fees to help defray the cost of publication". Many articles are written every month in numerous specialized magazines in which the authors tour the country from lodge to lodge and camp to camp sponsored, invited, or otherwise compensated in many different shapes or forms.

It is indeed a form of direct advertising and, although this type of writing usually conveys a good amount of general information, in most cases it lacks the impartiality so valuable when it comes time to make the final selection for your vacation or outdoor adventure.

Without belittling the invaluable job of the professional writers and their integrity, we decided to approach the task of **researching information and sharing it with the public** with a different angle and from an opposite direction.

## Money? .. No thanks!

We are firmly **committed to preserve the impartiality** and the novelty of the Picked-By-You idea.

For this reason we want to reassure the reader that the outdoor professionals and businesses featured in this book have not paid (nor will they pay), any remuneration to Picked-by-You Guides ® or the author in the form of money, invitations or any other considerations.

They have earned a valued page in this book solely as the result of *their hard work and dedication to their clients.*

**"A spot in this book cannot be purchased: it must be earned"**

## Size of a business in not a function of its performance

Since the embryonic stage of the Picked-By-You idea, during the compilation of the first Picked-By-You book, we faced a puzzling dilemma.

Should we establish a minimum number of clients under which a business or outdoor professional will not be allowed to participate in our evaluating process?

This would be a 'safe' decision when it comes the time to elaborate the responses of the questionnaires. But we quickly learned that many outdoor professionals limit, by choice, the total number of clients and, by philosophy of life, contain and control the size of their business. They do not want to grow too big and sacrifice the personal touches or the freshness of their services. In their words "we don't want to take the chance to get burned out by people." They do not consider their activity just a job, but rather a way of living.

"WHY, NO MAAM, WE NEVER HAVE HAD ANY OF THOSE SASQUATCH SIGHTINGS IN THESE PARTS."

But if this approach greatly limits the number of clients accepted every year we must say that these outdoor professionals are the ones who often receive outstanding ratings and truly touching comments from their past clients.

Some businesses have provided us with a list of clients of 40,000, some with 25 . In this book **you will find both the large and the small.**

From a statistical point, it is obvious that a fly fishing guide who submitted a list of 32 clients, by virtue of the sample size of the individuals surveyed, will implicitly have a lower level of accuracy if compared to a business for which we surveyed 300 guests. (Please refer to the Rating and Data

Elaboration Sections for details on how we established the rules for qualification and thus operated our selection).

We do not believe that the size of business is a function of its good performance and we feel strongly that those dedicated professionals who choose to remain small deserve an equal chance to be included.

## We tip our hats

We want to recognize all the Guides, Captains, Ranches, Lodges and Outfitters who have participated in our endeavor, whether they qualified or not. The fact alone that they accepted to be rated by their past clients is a clear indication of how much they care, and how willing they are to make changes.

We also want to credit all those outdoor enthusiasts who have taken the time to complete the questionnaires and share their memories and impressions with us and thus with you. Some of the comments sent to us were hilarious, some were truly touching.

We were immensely pleased by the reaction of the outdoor community at large. The idea of "Picked-by-You Guides®" was supported from the beginning by serious professionals and outdoor enthusiasts alike. We listened to their suggestions, their comments, their criticisms and we are now happy to share this information with you.

## Questionnaires

"Our books will be only as good as the questions we ask."

We posted this phrase in the office as a reminder of the importance of the 'tool' of this trade. The questions.

Specific Questionnaires were tailored to each one of the different activities surveyed for this series of books. While a few of the general questions remained the same throughout, many were specific to particular activities. The final objective of the questionnaire was to probe the many different facets of that diversified field known as the outdoors.

The first important factor we had to consider in the preparation of the Questionnaires was the total number of questions to be asked. Research shows an *inversely proportionate relation* between the total number of questions and the percentage of the response: the higher the number of questions, the lower the level of response. Thus we had to balance an acceptable return rate with a meaningful significance. We settled for a compromise and we decided to keep 20 as the maximum number.

The first and the final versions of the Questionnaires on which we based our surveys turned out to be very different. We asked all the businesses and outdoor professionals we contacted for suggestions and criticisms. They helped us a great deal: we weighed their different points of view and we incorporated all their suggestions into the final versions.

We initially considered using a phone survey, but we quickly agreed with the businesses and outdoor professional that we all are already bothered by too many solicitation calls when we are trying to have a quiet dinner at home. We do not want you to add Picked-By-You to the list of companies that you do not want to talk to, nor we want you to add our 800 number to your caller ID black list.

In using the mail we knew that we were going to have a slightly lower percentage of questionnaires answered, but this method is, in our opinion, a more respectful one.

We also encouraged the public to participate in the designing of the questionnaire by posting on our Web at www.topguides.com the opportunity to submit a question and ...."Win a book". Many sent their suggestions and , if they were chosen to be used in one of our questionnaires, they were given the book of their choice.

Please send us your question and/or your suggestions for our future surveys at:

PICKED-BY-YOU Guides®, P.O. Box 718, Baker City, OR 97814

# Rating (there is more than one way to skin the cat)

We considered many different ways to score the questionnaires, keeping in mind at all times our task:

**translate an opinion into a numerical value**

Some of the approaches considered were simple *averages* [arithmetical means], others were sophisticated statistical tests. In the end we opted for simplicity, sacrificing to the God of statistical significance. WARNING: if $p \leq 0.001$ has any meaning in your life stop reading right here: you will be disappointed with the rest.

For the rest of us, we also made extensive use in our computation of the *median*, a statistic of location, which divides the frequency distribution of a set of data into two halves. A quick example, with our imaginary Happy Goose Outfitter, will illustrate how in many instances the *median* value, being the center observation, helps describing the distribution, which is the truly weak point of the *average*:

*Average* salary at Happy Goose Outfitters $ 21,571

*Median* salary at Happy Goose Outfitters $ 11,000

| 5,000 | 10,000 | 10,000 | 11,000 | 12,000 | 15,000 | 98,000 |
|---|---|---|---|---|---|---|
| Wrangler | Guide | Guide | Senior Guide | Asst.Cook | Cook | Boss |

Do not ask the boss : "What's the average salary?"

These are the values assigned to **Questions 1-15**:

    5.00 points    OUTSTANDING

    4.75 points    EXCELLENT

    4.25 points    GOOD

    3.50 points    ACCEPTABLE

    3.00 points    POOR

    0.00 points    UNACCEPTABLE

**Question 16**, relating to the weather conditions, was treated as bonus points to be added to the final score.

    Good=0        Fair=1        Poor=2

The intention here was to reward the outdoor professional who had to work in adverse weather conditions.

    **Questions 17 - 18** = 5 points

    **Questions 19 - 20** = 10 points

The individual scores of each Questionnaire were expressed as a percentage to avoid the total score from being drastically affected by one question left unanswered or marked "not applicable." All the scores received for each individual outdoor professional and business were thus added and computed.

The 90 points were considered our cutoff point. Note how the outfitters must receive a combination of Excellent with only a few Good marks (or better) in order to qualify.

**Only the Outfitters, Captains, Lodges, Guides who received an A- to A+ score did qualify and they are featured in this book.**

We also decided not to report in the book pages the final scores with which the businesses and the outdoor professionals ultimately qualified. In a way we thought that this could be distractive.

In the end, we must admit, it was tough to leave out some outfitters who scored very close to the cutoff mark.

It would be presumptuous to think that our scoring system will please everybody, but we want to assure the reader that we tested different computations of the data. We feel the system that we have chosen respects the overall opinion of the guest/client and maintains a more than acceptable level of accuracy.

We know that …. "You can change without improving, but you cannot improve without changing."

## The Power of Graphs (how to lie by telling the scientific truth)

The following examples illustrate the sensational (and unethical) way with which the 'scientific' computation of data can be distorted to suit one's needs or goals.

The *Herald* presents a feature article on the drastic increase of total tonnage of honey stolen by bears (mostly Poohs) in a given area during 1997.

### Total tonnage of honey stolen by bears (Poohs)

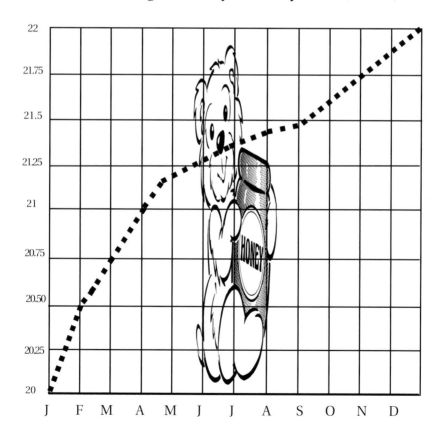

## Total tonnage of honey stolen by bears (Poohs)

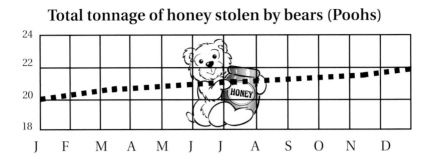

It is clear how a journalist, researcher or author must ultimately choose one type of graph. But the question here is whether or not he/she is trying to make "his/her point" by choosing one type versus the other, rather than simply communicate some findings.

Please note that the bears, in our example, are shameless, and remain such in both instances, for they truly love honey!

Graphs were not used in this book. We were just too worried we wouldn't use the correct ones.

# The Book Making Process

## Research

We **researched** the name and address of every business and outdoor professional **in the United States and** in all the **provinces of Canada** (see list in the Appendix). Some states do not require guides and outfitters or businesses providing outdoor services to be registered, and in these instances the information must be obtained from many different sources [Outfitter's Associations, Marine Fisheries, Dept. of Tourism, Dept. Environmental Conservation, Dept. of Natural Resources, Dept. of Fish and Game, US Coast Guard, Chamber of Commerce, etc.].

In the end the database on which we based this series of Picked-By-You Guides® amounted to more than 23,000 names of Outfitters, Guides, Ranches, Captains etc. Our research continues and this number is increasing every day. The Appendix in the back of this book is only a partial list and refers specifically to Top Rated Rocky Mountain Adventures.

## Participation

We **invited** businesses and outdoor professionals, with a letter and a brochure explaining the Picked-By-You concept, to join our endeavor by simply sending us a **complete list of their clients** of the past two years. With the "Confidentiality Statement" we reassured them that the list was going to be kept **absolutely confidential** and to be *used one time only* for the specific purpose of evaluating their operation. Then it would be destroyed.

We truly oppose this "black market" of names so abused by the mail marketing business. If you are ever contacted by Picked-By-You you may rest assured that your name, referred to us by your outdoor professional, will never be sold, traded or otherwise used a second time by us for marketing purposes.

## Questionnaires

We then **sent a questionnaire** to **every single client on each list** (to a maximum of 300 randomly picked for those who submitted large lists with priority given to overnight or multiple day trips), asking them to rate the

**services**, the **knowledge** and **performance** of the business or outdoor professional by completing our comprehensive questionnaire (see pages 266-267). The businesses and outdoor professionals found in these pages may or may not be the ones who invest large sums of money to advertise in magazines, or to participate at the annual conventions of different clubs and foundations. However, they are clearly the ones, according to our survey, that put customer satisfaction and true dedication to their clients first and foremost.

## Data Elaboration

A **numerical value was assigned to each question**. All the **scores were computed**. Both the **average** and the **median** were calculated and considered for eligibility. Please note that the total score was computed as a percentile value.

This allows some flexibility where one question was left unanswered or was answered with a N/A. Furthermore, we decided not to consider the high and the low score to ensure a more evenly distributed representation and to reduce the influence which an extreme judgement could have either way (especially with the small sample sizes).

We also set a **minimum number of questionnaires** which needed to be answered to allow a business or an outdoor professional to qualify. Such number was set as a function of the total number of clients in the list: the smaller the list of clients, the higher was the percentage of responses needed for qualification.

In some cases the outfitter's average score came within 1 points of the A-cutoff mark. In these instances, we considered both the median and the average were considered as well as the guests' comments and the total number of times that this particular business was recommended by the clients by answering with a 'yes' question 19 and 20.

## Sharing the results

**Picked-By-You will share the results of this survey with the businesses and the outdoor professionals.** This will be done at no cost to them whether or not they qualified for publication. All questionnaires received will, in fact, be returned along with a summary result to the business, keeping the confidentiality of the client's name when this was requested. This will prove an invaluable tool to help improving those areas that have received some criticisms.

The intention of this series of books is to research the opinions and the comments of outdoor enthusiasts, and to share the results of our research with the public and other key groups.

One outfitter wrote us about our Picked-by-You Guides® series, "I feel your idea is an exciting and unique concept. Hopefully our past clientele will rate us with enough points to 'earn' a spot in your publication. If not, could we please get a copy of our points/questionnaires to see where we need to improve. Sincerely…"

This outfitter failed to qualify by just a few points, but such willingness to improve leaves us no doubt that his/her name will be one of those featured in our second edition. In the end it was not easy to exclude some of them from publication, but we are certain that, with the feedback provided by this survey, they will be able to improve those areas that need extra attention.

We made a real effort to keep a position of absolute impartiality in this process and, in this respect, we would like to repeat that the outfitters have not paid, nor they will pay, one single penny to Picked-By-You Guides® or the Author to be included in this book.

The research continues.

# Icon Legend
## General Services and Accommodations

Family

Kids

Senior Citizen

Handicap

Women Only Camps/Dates

Drop Camp

Spike Tent Camp

Hot Springs/Spas

Swimming Pool

Archeological Sites

Tennis

Lodge

Cabin

Wall Tent Camp

Full Board

Sleep Aboard

Trailer

Natural /Gourmet Meals

Hotel/Motel

# Icon Legend - Big Game Hunting
## Weapons and Transportation

Rifle

Bow

Muzzleloader

Handgun

Bush plane

ATV

Snowmobile

Drift Boat

4 x 4 Vehicle

Horse/Pack String

Canoe

Back Packer

Raft

Motor Boat/Jet Boat

Motor Yacht/Cabin Cruiser

# Icon Legend
## General Services

Unguided Activities

Guided Activities

Overnight Trips

Fish Cleaning
Service

Day Trips

## Season(s) of Operation

Fall

Year-round

Summer

Winter

Spring

# Icon Legend
## Locations

Blue Ribbon Stream

Blue Ribbon Waterway

River Delta

Saltwater

Estuary

Lake

Open Ocean

Pond

Large River

Stream

Marsh/Wetlands

# Icon Legend
## River Classes of Difficulty

# Icon Legend
## Schools

Horse Packing School

Horse Shoeing School

Horse Riding School

Raft/Kayak School

Fly Tying School

Fly Fishing School

# Icon Legend
## Activities /Fishing Techniques

Catch and Release

Fly Fishing

Skinny Fishing (flats, bays)

River Fishing with Dory

Whitewater Trips

River Fishing with Raft

Spin Casting

Trophy Fishing

Deep Water Fishing

Whale Watching

Crabbing /Shrimping

Bird Watching

Wildlife Viewing

# Icon Legend
## Activities

Sporting Clay,
Trap, Skeet

Big Game Hunting

Bird Hunting

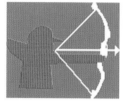

Bow Hunting/Archery

Rifle Hunting/Target
Shooting

Trekking /Backpacking

Cross Country Skiing

Snow Shoeing

Mountain Biking

Golfing

Dancing

ATV Tours/Rentals

Cowboy and Live
Entertainment

Snowmobile Riding

# Icon Legend
## Activities

Horseback Riding

Llama Pack Trips

Pack Trips

Barrel Racing

Roping

Team Roping

Team Penning

Steer Wrestling

Wagon Rides

Ghost Town Tours

Branding

Cutting

Cattle / Horse Drives

# Icon Legend

## Big Game

**White Tail Deer**
*(Odocoileus virginianus)*

**Mule Deer**
*(Odocoileus hemionus)*

**Black Tail Deer**
*(Odocoileus hemionus columbianus)*

**Sitka Deer**
*(Odocoileus hemionus)*

**Coues' Deer**
*(Odocoileus virginianus couesi)*

**Antelope**
*(Antilocapra americana)*

**Moose**
*(Alces alces)*

**Elk**
*(Cervus elaphus canadensis)*

**Bighorn Sheep**
*(Ovis canadensis canadensis)*

**Stone's Sheep**
*(Ovis dalli stonei)*

**Desert Bighorn Sheep**
*(Ovis canadensis nelsoni)*

**Dall's Sheep**
*(Ovis dalli dalli)*

# Icon Legend
## Big Game

**Mountain Goat**
*(Oreamnos americanus)*

**Caribou**
*(Rangifer sp.)*

**Black Bear**
*(Ursus arctos)*

**Brown Bear**
*(Ursus middendorfii)\**

**Grizzly Bear**
*(Ursus horribilis)\**

**Polar Bear**
*(Thalarctos maritimus)*

**Wolf**
*(Canis lupus)*

**Wolverine**
*(Gulo luscus)*

**Cougar**
*(Felis concolor)*

**Bobcat**
*(Lynx rufus)*

**Coyote**
*(Canis latrans)*

**Javelina**
*(Pecari angulatus)*

**Bison**
*(Bison bison)*

**Wild Boar**
*(Sus scrofa)*

*Modern taxonomists recognize both Grizzly and Brown Bear as 1 specie, *Ursus arctos*.

# Icon Legend
## Fish

Largemouth Bass

Crappie(s)

Smallmouth Bass

Muskellunge

Striped Bass

Northern Pike

Bluegill

Perch(es)

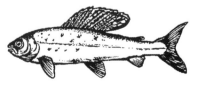

Arctic Grayling

Arctic Char

# Icon Legend
## Fish

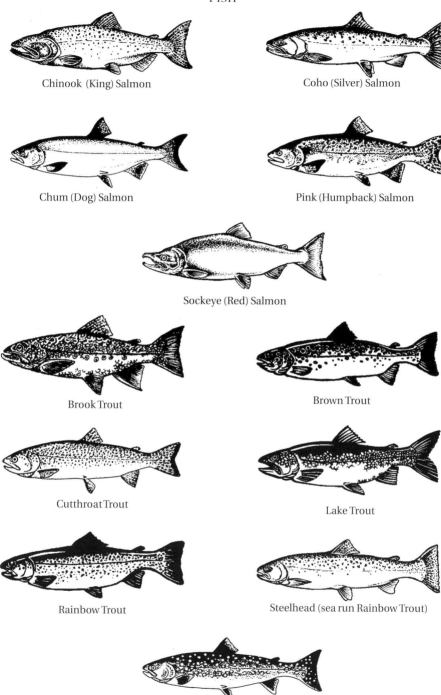

Chinook (King) Salmon

Coho (Silver) Salmon

Chum (Dog) Salmon

Pink (Humpback) Salmon

Sockeye (Red) Salmon

Brook Trout

Brown Trout

Cutthroat Trout

Lake Trout

Rainbow Trout

Steelhead (sea run Rainbow Trout)

Dolly Varden

# Icon Legend
## Boat Types and Transportation

Airplane on Floaters

Dory / McKenzie River Boat

Inflatable Kayak

Cataraft

Canoe

Raft

Bass Boat

Motor Boat

Jon Boat

Pontoon Motorboat

Jet Boat

Open Console Boat

# Top Rated
# Big Game Hunting
## Outfitters and Guides

# 4 + 2 T Ranch

**Craig T. Tomke**
P.O. Box 896 • Hayden, CO 81639
phone/fax: (970) 276-4283 • cellular: (970) 846-3780
Lic. #868

Our main goal is that our guests are completely satisfied with every aspect of our operation. We enjoy an 80%-plus re-book from our guests and feel we our meeting our goals of "high quality" and "first-class" service. By hunting the largest elk herd in the world, we also provide some of the highest success on 4x4 or better bulls <u>anywhere</u> !

We have always listed <u>everyone</u> who hunts with us as references every year.

If your goal is a first-class hunt in a tremendous game country — please contact us and we will help plan the hunt you will remember forever.

We have been in business 11 years and hunt both private and public land.

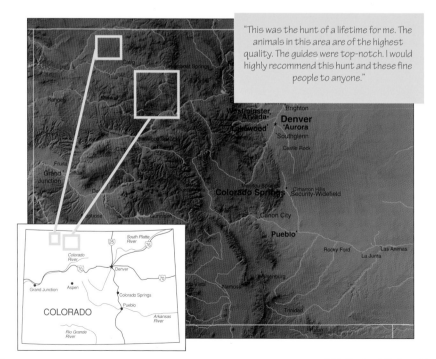

"This was the hunt of a lifetime for me. The animals in this area are of the highest quality. The guides were top-notch. I would highly recommend this hunt and these fine people to anyone."

# A/Z Outfitters, Ltd.

**Bill DuBois**
Box 86 • Windermere, B.C., Canada V0B 2L0
phone: (604) 342-3935

We offer un-roaded wilderness horse hunts in Southeast British Columbia. Beautiful country, log cabin camps, excellent guides and trophy wildlife. Specializing in elk, mountain goat, grizzly and black bear. Also offering hunts for the Shiras moose, mule deer and cougar.

We have 18 years' experience in the same area with the bulk of our clients being either repeats or referrals. Our hunts are ten days with one experienced guide for each hunter and seldom more than three hunters in the same camp.

We offer a total hunting and wilderness experience which will give you the opportunity to forget the pressure of business, to relax, and at the same time, enjoy a highly successful hunt.

"One of the finest outfitters and guides I have ever had."

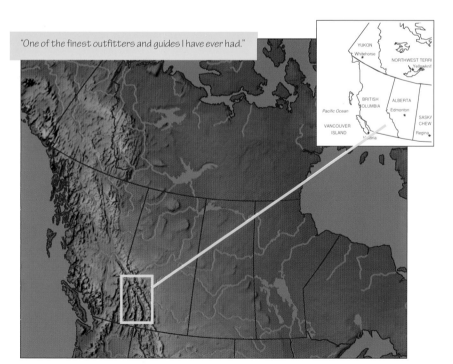

# Arrowhead Outfitters

**Robert Lowe**
P.O. Box 835 • Jackson Hole, WY 83001
ph. (307) 733-5223

Bobby Lowe has been guiding/outfitting in Wyoming since 1976. He takes pride being able to offer hunters a top-quality, personalized hunt.

He services a low volume of hunters to keep success and satisfaction at a maximum.

Arrowhead Outfitters operates two Bridger Wilderness area camps. Guides are friendly, experienced and knowledgeable.

Excellent mountain horses and mules accommodate even inexperienced riders. Tents, saddles and equipment are all in top shape. Game populations in the areas are some of the best in Wyoming to give you the best chance possible to take home your trophy animal. Color brochure available.

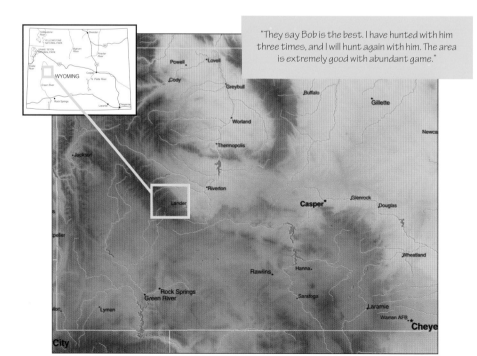

"They say Bob is the best. I have hunted with him three times, and I will hunt again with him. The area is extremely good with abundant game."

# Beaver Creek Outfitters

**Steve Kobold**

PO Box 7337 • Sheridan, WY 82801
ph. (307) 672-0008

Beaver Creek Outfitters have been in business for 13 years. We offer elk, antelope and mule deer and, occasionally, buffalo and moose hunts. We take a limited number of hunters each year as we want to assure our customer the best possible hunt.

Over the last three years, our elk have an average score of 341, with two making the Boone and Crockett record book. All of our hunts are on private land consisting of more than 250,000 acres near historic Hole-in-the-Wall district of Northern Wyoming.

We are very close to our hunting areas so our hunters stay in a motel. We gladly accommodate handicapped hunters.

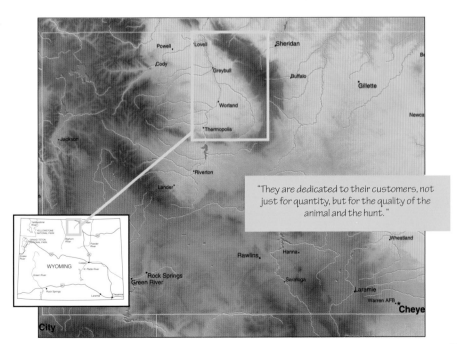

"They are dedicated to their customers, not just for quantity, but for the quality of the animal and the hunt."

# Big Rack Adventures

**Blair and Kathy Trout**

Box 98 • Newbrook, Alberta, Canada T0A 2P0
ph. (403) 576-2394

We, Blair and Kathy, offer one of the finest quality whitetail deer and black bear hunts in Alberta. We have been in the business since the early '80s, maintaining only the highest hunting and fair chase ethics.

We provide our clients with top-quality service, attending to the smallest of details. Our lodge provides real home-like atmosphere. We hunt the fringe area between agricultural and big bush country on public and private land. Extensive scouting and shed-antler hunting enables us to determine the location and the quality of the game in our area. We had previously picked up at least one shed from half of the bucks taken in the '95 season.

We provide complete trophy care. Our overall goal is for a top quality hunt and a top quality trophy.

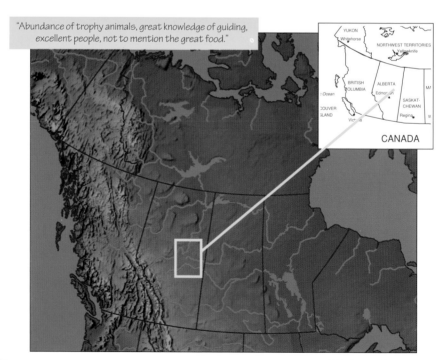

"Abundance of trophy animals, great knowledge of guiding, excellent people, not to mention the great food."

# Bonnet Plume Outfitters, Ltd.

**Charlie Stricker**

P.O. Box 5963 • Whitehorse, Yukon Territories, Canada Y1A 5L7
phone/fax: (403) 633-3366

Located in the northeast portion of the Yukon against the Northwest Territories border, in Outfitting Area #5 and Game Management Zone 2. The area is noted as a good producer of good-quality game in horns and antlers for Dall's sheep, moose, Barrenground and mountain caribou. Also grizzly, black bear, wolf, and wolverine.

Being very remote we have never seen another hunter who was not with our outfit. All hunters fly to Whitehorse and then are moved to my base camp the next day by bush plane.

I have six base camps in a 100-mile stretch of wilderness. Plus, there are six different hunts for you to choose and experience the Yukon wilderness.

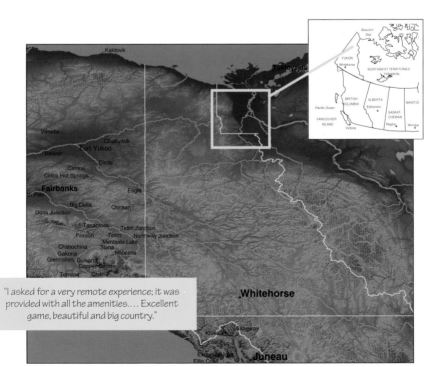

"I asked for a very remote experience; it was provided with all the amenities.... Excellent game, beautiful and big country."

# Boulder Lake Lodge

**Kim Bright**
Box 1100 • Pinedale, WY 82941
ph. (307) 537-5400 or (800) 788-5401

The Boulder Lake Lodge is one of the oldest and most successful hunting-outfitting operations in the state of Wyoming. It is located in the heart of the Bridger National Forest in the Wind River Range of the Rocky Mountains.

The ranch features a beautiful and rustic lodge, which serves as base camp for hunting operations.

It is located in the center of some of the state's finest big game areas. Boulder Lake Lodge not only provides the best hunting and hunting areas, but you also receive fine food, accommodations and hospitality.

"I have hunted at Boulder Lake Ranch three times in the last four years and always been pleased with every aspect of the operation."

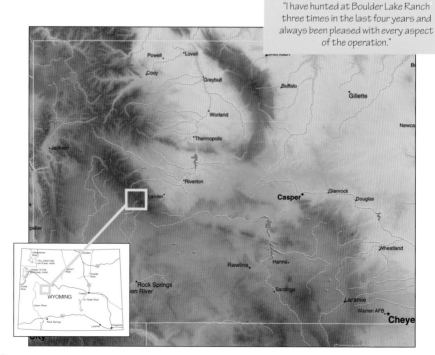

# Buckhorn Ranch Outfitters

## Harry and Claire Workman

Box 84 • Eureka, MT 59917
ph. (406) 889-3762

Harry and Claire Workman's Buckhorn Ranch Outfitters, is a family-owned and operated outfit with 30 years in the Bob Marshall Wilderness and a lifetime experience in beautiful northwestern Montana. Buckhorn Ranch 10-day wilderness hunts take place in the Silvertip Creek drainage of the Bob Marshall Wilderness, Flathead National Forest. Most of the summer pack trip and the deer, moose, and bear hunts are near our home ranch in Eureka, Montana. Silvertip City's remote wilderness hunting camp has been in continuous operation for more than 50 years with the "over 80" retired outfitter, who established the camp, still helping out!

From this camp we hunt primarily elk but also mule deer, black bear, goats and moose.

Whether it is a day ride from the ranch or a 10-day wilderness hunt, Buckhorn Ranch's Montana outing is an exciting, enjoyable adventure.

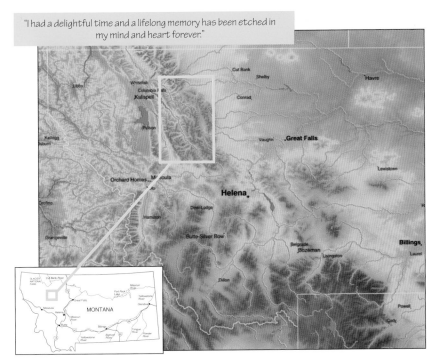

"I had a delightful time and a lifelong memory has been etched in my mind and heart forever."

# Cariboo Mountain Outfitters

## Bradley Bowden
Box 4010 • Quesnel, B.C., Canada V2J 3J2
phone: (604) 747-3334 • fax: (604) 747-3020

Cariboo Mountain base camp is 31 miles east of Quesnel, situated on a 3,000-foot meadow along Victoria Creek. It consists of log cabins with wood stoves, propane lights, running water and bath facilities. The guide area covers 700 square miles between Quesnel and the historic town of Bakerville. Hunts are conducted by horse, four-wheel-drive, and jet boat.

This is a family-run operation; I personally guide every client for part of their hunt. I limit my clients to a maximum of four per hunt to ensure the best success.

I have been guiding in this area for 29 years. Please call for further information.

"Makes every effort to satisfy the hunter and get you in range to shoot. Great people. I've hunted 15 years with this outfitter."

# Castle Creek Outfitters

## Shane McAfee

P.O. Box 2008 • Salmon, ID 83467
phone: (208) 756-2548

Castle Creek Outfitters is owned and operated by Shane R. McAfee.

We have over 70,000 acres licensed to us by the State of Idaho in which Shane has been guiding hunters for over 24 years.

Castle Creek only takes a limited number of hunters each year in order to keep our hunts the highest quality.

We offer 2 types of hunts. You can hunt out of log cabin bunk houses from our back country ranch or you can pack into our deluxe tent camp.

We offer both 1 on 1, or 1 on 2, 8 day hunts from both locations.

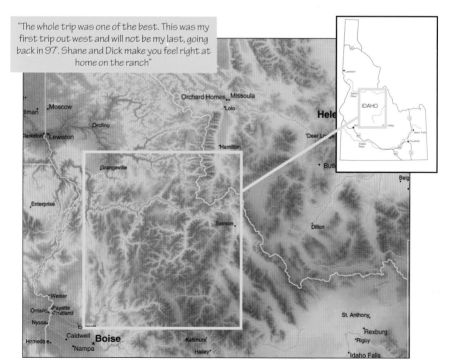

"The whole trip was one of the best. This was my first trip out west and will not be my last, going back in 97. Shane and Dick make you feel right at home on the ranch"

# Cecil Ralston Guides and Outfitters

**Cecil and Jodie Ralston**
P.O. Box 1510 • Bernalillo, NM 87004
ph. (505) 867-2191

We offer hunts for mule deer, black bear, mountain lion, antelope, javelina, Barbary sheep, bighorn sheep, oryx and ibex.

We have a two-on-one guide system, while arrangements can be made for anyone who requests a personal guide. We hunt both public and private land, using horses, 4x4 trucks, four-runners, and some on foot. Most all of our hunts are based on five days; some are longer and some are two to three days. Our camps are comfortable, wall tents, lights, cots and stoves. All meals are good and wholesome, family style home cooked meals all you can eat. We cater to our hunters as much as possible.

Our main interest is you. If you drive out you can come here to our house, or the ones that fly can be picked up at the Albuquerque International Airport.

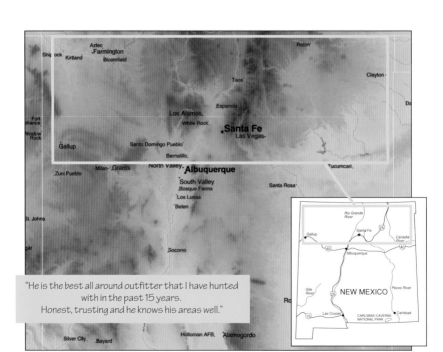

"He is the best all around outfitter that I have hunted with in the past 15 years. Honest, trusting and he knows his areas well."

# Chase Hill Outfitters

## Bill and Renita Brown

HC77 Box 851 • Big Sandy, MT 59520
ph. (406) 386-2447 • fax (406) 386-2435

Chase Hill Outfitters specializes in Pope and Young bull elk, trophy deer and varmint safaris. The quantity and quality of animals is tremendous with one-to-one doe-buck ratio on the mule deer end the with the elk rated No. 1 in North America.

Our guides are all professionals; courteous, ambitious and knowledgeable. Our fleet vehicles consist of 4x4 4-door trucks and Suburbans. The hunts are all guided on more than 100,000 acres of exclusively-leased or owned private land, and 2 million acres of public land.

We have very spacious ranch-style accommodations with a large recreation room, three bedrooms and two bathrooms. The meals are big, hearty, all-you-can-eat, with homemade breads and gourmet desserts.

"I have never seen more elk in my life nor I have ever been so close to them. It was great."

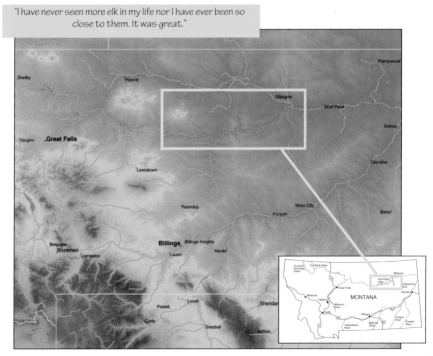

# Cow Creek Outfitters

**John Fritz**

Box 280 • Chester, MT 59522
ph./fax (406) 432-2755

Cow Creek Outfitters is located on a working cattle ranch 47 miles south of Chinook, Montana.

We do not advertise but in the eight years we have been professionally guiding, we have depended completely on the recommendations of our past clients.

I am proud to say we offer some of the best mule deer and antelope hunting in Montana. We have good elk and bighorn sheep populations with permits by drawings. We hunt a huge area of approximately 20-square miles.

The area consists of the Bear Paw Mountains on the north and the Badlands and canyons of the Missouri River Breaks on the south.

"John and Bob Fritz are as honest and forthright an outfitter as you could hope to find anywhere. ... Once my party arrived at Cow Creek we were treated like family, probably better in some cases!"

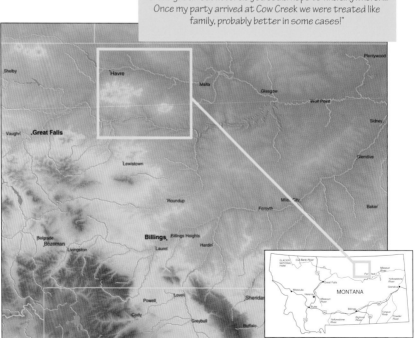

# Darby Mountain Outfitters

## John Harper and Chuck Thornton

Box 447 • Big Piney, WY 83113
ph. (307) 386-9220 • (307) 276-3934

Come to beautiful Wyoming and enjoy quality, first-class full service hunting at an affordable price. All hunts include food, comfortable wall tent lodging, bath tent, airport shuttle, trophy care, experienced and gentle mountain horses with tack.

Our guides (with two hunters per guide) are dedicated professionals who work hard to ensure a successful hunt. At Darby Mountain Outfitters we put forth the extra effort (experience blended with personal service) to assure you will enjoy your stay with us.

We want you to enjoy your vacation and want it to be an experience worth returning to.

We do our very best to show you success and good time.

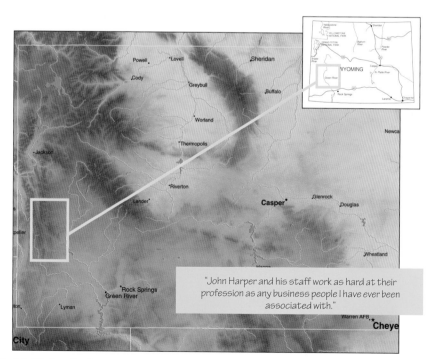

"John Harper and his staff work as hard at their profession as any business people I have ever been associated with."

# Darwin Ranch

**Loring Woodman**

PO Box 511 • Jackson, WY 83001
ph. (307) 733-5588 • Fax (307) 739-0885

The Darwin Ranch has been catering to hunters ever since 1965 when Loring Woodman started renovating the old log cabins along the original, now obliterated, pioneer wagon track into Jackson Hole.

We are 22 miles inside the Teton National Forest and have this last, totally isolated section of the Gros Ventre River to ourselves, giving us excellent access to the area's resident elk and moose populations.

Maximum of six hunters at a time with one guide for every two hunters.

A wilderness hunt with success rates of 80-85% on elk and 100% on moose in the last 30 years.

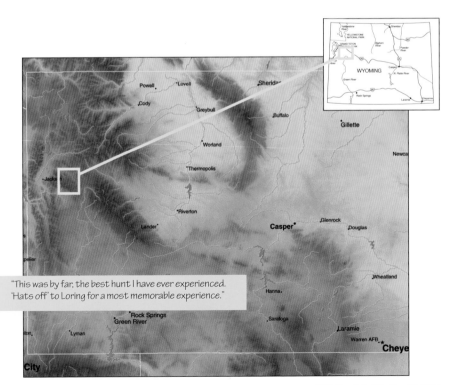

"This was by far, the best hunt I have ever experienced. 'Hats off' to Loring for a most memorable experience."

# Double J Outfitters

**Jimmy and Jenny Heap**
P.O. Box 990 • St. Johns, AZ 85936
phone: 520-337-2339 • 505-533-6515

We are Jimmy and Jenny Heap of the NH Ranch. We are small and intend to stay that way.

We specialize in friendly, personalized service and superior quality hunts. This is not your run-of-the-mill hunting trip.

We have been in business three years and offer private landowner and public hunts. Our guides have been screened and especially selected. Ratios are one-to-one.

Prices are fair with no "extra" fees. We promise wonderful food, hot showers and warm and comfortable beds. Our services are unsurpassed.

Come hunt with Double J and get set for good times, great hunting and big bulls.

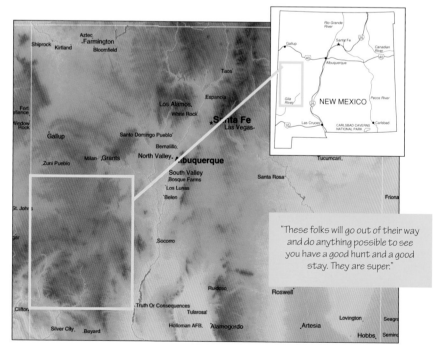

"These folks will go out of their way and do anything possible to see you have a good hunt and a good stay. They are super."

# Echo Canyon Guest Ranch & Outfitters

## David Hampton

P.O. Box 328 • La Veta, CO 81055
phone: (800) 341-6603 • (719) 742-5524 • Lic. #1143

Echo Canyon Outfitters provides first-class trophy-quality hunts on a private ranch in Unit 851 of Southern Colorado. Our hunters are guided one-on-one by experienced guides who are very knowledgeable of the terrain and wildlife. The hunts are extremely professional, offering quality accommodations, food, stock, and personnel.

We are active members of Rocky Mountain Elk Foundation as sponsors, donors and habitat partners. Our Long Canyon Ranch is strictly managed for wildlife habitat and trophy-class production under a conservation easement with RMEF. The outfit brings 11 years' of solid experience to our business. We annually re-book more than 75% of our clients two years in advance.

We specialize in trophy elk and mule deer, black bear, mountain lion and turkey.

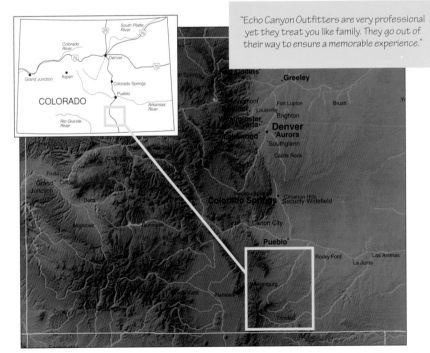

"Echo Canyon Outfitters are very professional yet they treat you like family. They go out of their way to ensure a memorable experience."

# Elk Creek Outfitting

**Brent and Kathy Fitchett**
20 W. Elk Creek Road • Heron, MT 59844
ph. (406) 847-5593

Welcome to Elk Creek Outfitting located in the mountainous border between Northwestern Montana and Northeastern Idaho.

With a comfortable lodge, cozy cabins and home-cooked meals, owners and operators Brent and Kathy Fitchett will make your stay memorable. Elk Creek Outfitting is licensed and bonded to hunt big game animals in Montana and Idaho.

For a wide variety of hunts Elk Creek Outfitting has rifle, archery and muzzleloader hunts for elk, bear, mountain lion, whitetail and mule deer (moose and sheep available by special drawings). Elk Creek Outfitting also hunts on the Kootenai National Forest in Montana, and on the Panhandle National Forest in Idaho, and they offer exclusive trophy whitetail deer hunts on private land in Montana.

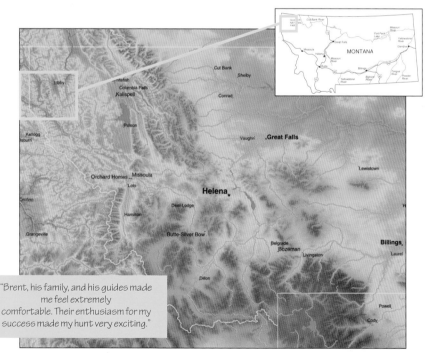

"Brent, his family, and his guides made me feel extremely comfortable. Their enthusiasm for my success made my hunt very exciting."

PBY - Top Rated Big Game Hunting

# Esper's Under Wild Skies Lodge and Outfitters

**Vaughn Esper**
P.O. Box 849 • Philipsburg, MT 59858
ph. (406) 859-3000

Under Wild Skies Lodge & Outfitters is located in Anaconda Pintler Wilderness and surrounding Deer Lodge and Beaverhead National Forests. It has exclusive hunting rights in 300,000 acres of some of the best hunting in Southwestern Montana.

Our courteous, trained, licensed and seasoned guides are professionals with the highest standards. They take great pride in their abilities and success rates. At Under Wild Skies, we pay meticulous attention to every detail and make every effort to make your hunt productive and memorable, and it shows.

At the end of the trail where the mountains meet the sky, you will find "the last best place"…Under Wild Skies.

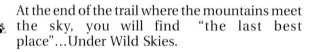

"The personnel at Esper's Under Wild Skies took their time to teach us how to read signs, to rub down a horse, identify land marks, etc. I would definitely go there again."

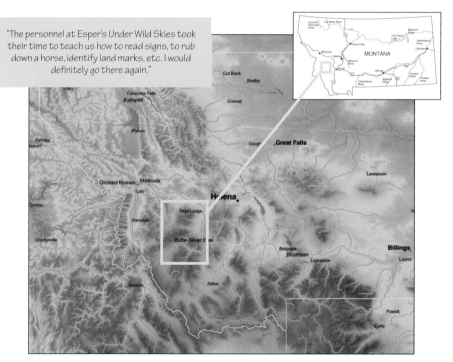

# EW Watson & Sons Outfitting

## Ed and Wanda Watson

7837 U.S. Hwy. 287 • Townsend, MT 59644
phone: (800) 654-2845 • fax: (406) 266-4498

Ours is a family-owned and operated business which specializes in custom outdoor adventures. This is traditional elk/deer hunting at its finest.

Sixteen years of guiding and pack experience have given us the extra ability it takes to produce trophies for our clients. Service and quality are our main goals!

The unique geography of our area in the Lee Metcalf Wilderness in the Beaverhead National Forest of the Madison Mountain Range near Ennis, Mont., makes for very little hunting pressure and excellent game opportunities. This is one hunt you don't want to miss.

We look forward to a quality hunting experience with you.

"This was one of the most thought out and planned hunts I've been on! The cook was outstanding, my guide very knowledgeable, courteous and considerate of your wishes.... Truly a memorable hunting experience."

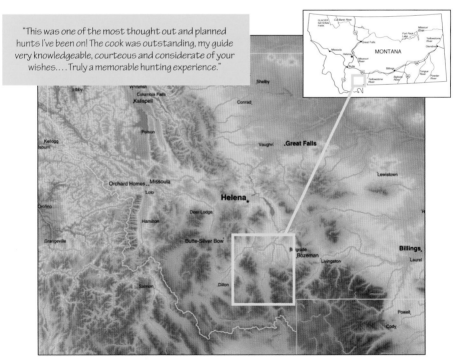

# Flat Iron Outfitting

**Jerry C. Shively**
3 Golf Course Rd. • Thompson Falls, MT  59873
ph. (406) 827-3666

Flat Iron Outfitting provides a very unique and personal service for hunters and fisherman and other people who want to experience the very best of western Montana.

We have a flatland lease which produces some of the finest whitetails in Montana.

The largest whitetail taken on a guided hunt in this state was taken here. Our Forest Service permit area has an excellent elk, bear, and cougar population.

Our high mountain lake fishing, photo trips and day hikes in the mountains make for a lifetime of unforgettable memories.

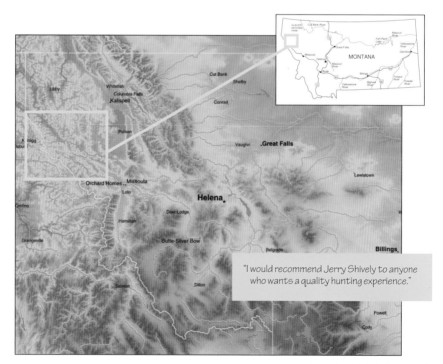

"I would recommend Jerry Shively to anyone who wants a quality hunting experience."

# Frazier Outfitting

**Sammy Frazier**

HC 34, Box 81 • Rye, CO 81069

ph. (719) 676-2964 • Lic. #1738

Frazier Outfitting is located 40 miles southwest of Creede, Colorado, at the headwaters of the Rio Grande River. We operate in Unit 76, a limited draw area since 1986, where the bull cow ratio is 35 to 100.

We are a horseback operation offering muzzleloader, archery and rifle hunts. Hunting Unit 76 in the Rio Grande National Forest and Weminuche Wilderness at an alpine elevation of 10,000–13,000 feet, can be physically challenging for most individuals. In 1991, '94 and '95, our hunters received awards from the Colorado Outfitters Association for the "best elk taken." The majority of our hunters harvest quality bulls, taking 5x5 or better in all hunts.

We are a small business offering quality service and quality bulls.

"My hunt was incredible. Sammy Frazier was fantastic. I have been involved in several guided hunts and I would rate him as the finest guide for bull elk."

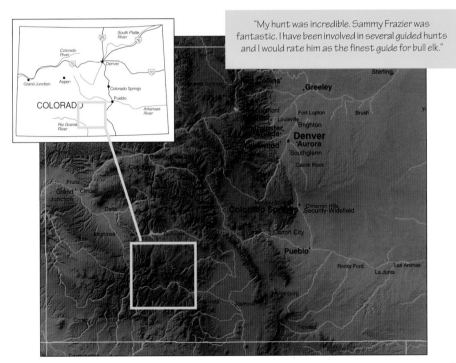

# Garvey Brothers Outfitters

## Stan Garvey
Box 555 • Nucla, CO 81424
phone: (970) 864-2243 • Lic. #606

Garvey Brothers Outfitters provides a full-service guided hunt. Giving you small camps, our motto is not the quantity of hunters but the quality of your hunt. Speaking of quality, the area we hunt (Unit 61) takes a minimum of three years for elk and two for deer in rifle season.

As this hunt has taken you years to plan, we would like to make it a hunt you have dreamed about.

Animals are spotted daily and the percentage of animals taken in the last three years is about 95%. We hunt both public and private lands.

Homemade food, fresh pies and bread baked daily make for a memorable hunt.

"This outfitter is a 'real' hunter. He knows the quarry, knows the area, and he has the ambition to go get them."

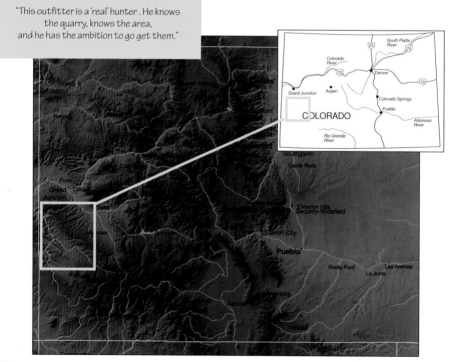

# Grand and Sierra Outfitters

**Glen Knotwell**
PO Box 312 • Encampment, WY 82325
ph. (307) 327-5200 or (307) 327-5107

**Skyler Knotwell**
2200 S. 558 W. • Oakley, ID 83346
ph. (208) 862-3872

Grand and Sierra Outfitters is a family owned business of forty years, that is based out of Encampment Wyoming.

We conduct our big trophy and game hunts on both private and public lands.

Hunts are from the lodge or tent camps depending on what species hunted or where you are going to hunt.

Fall-Big Game hunts Deer, Elk, Antelope and Sheep (remember that all Wyoming non-resident big game hunts are by drawing).

For more information, give us a call.

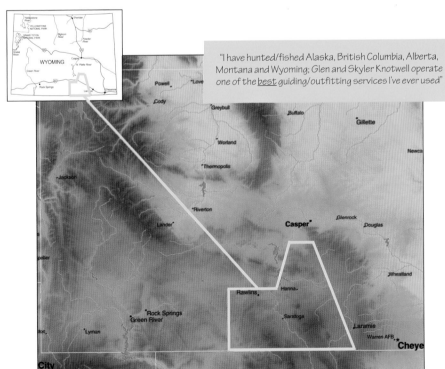

"I have hunted/fished Alaska, British Columbia, Alberta, Montana and Wyoming; Glen and Skyler Knotwell operate one of the _best_ guiding/outfitting services I've ever used"

# Greer Outfitters

**Randy and Lora Greer**

PO Box 38 • Gillette, WY 82717

ph. (307) 687-7461

Greer Outfitters is a family operation established in 1952. We offer exceptional Trophy Antelope, Mule Deer, Whitetail and Buffalo hunting.

We control 300,000 acres of PRIVATE property taking only a select amount of hunters every season. Our success rate is excellent on both rifle and archery. We offer professionally guided hunts as well as drop camps.

Not only is our quantity exceptional but our quality as well with an average season producing Mule Deer , 24" 5x5 up to 30", Antelope ranging from 14" to 16", and Whitetail 16" 5x5 up to 20".

We cater to individual needs and parties depending on ability and circumstances. We also offer private game bird hunting, trout fishing and welcome non-hunters.

"I have been on 200 guided hunts and Randy rates high among those whom I hunted with."

# Hebert's Guide Service

**Joe and Doreen Hebert**

Box 234 • Valleyview, Alberta, Canada T0H 3N0
ph. (403) 524-2417 • fax (403) 524-4725

We operate a family guide service at Little Smoky, a very small but active community with mostly farming and oil field work. Our farm is ten miles northwest of Little Smoky where we have our clients meet us.

Our hunts consist of parties of four or six people at one time, however, our facilities will accommodate more if required. Camp consist of three sleepers and a cookhouse with a fireplace. We use quads and Argos in wildlife management Unit 54 for elk, moose whitetail and mule deer, spring and fall bear. Also goose hunting in the early fall. Summer photography and scenic quad trips available. All guides are experienced.

We are licensed and bonded members of the P.O.A.A., Safari Club and fish and game. For your memorable hunting trips call or fax us in Alberta.

"I have sent many of my friends to the Hebert's as well as continuing to go myself. ... Great family operation."

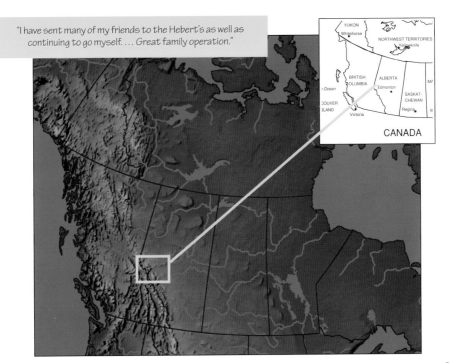

# Hidden Basin Outfitters

**Phillip Engler — George Engler**

P.O. Box 1146 • Jackson, WY 83001

ph. business: (307) 733-7980 • residence: (307) 733-1108

Hidden Basin is owned and operated by brothers who are lifetime natives of the area. Both have been hunting guides for more than 20 years.

Our camp is accessible by 4-wheel drive which makes it a very comfortable setup.

We are located on the Wyoming/Idaho border. When Idaho's season opens, it gives us a mid-season boost, driving the game back over to our area. In the summer months, we give horseback tours, which help us keep a close eye on the game.

Our camp is full with six hunters which helps to maintain a high success rate. We have a two-hunter to one-guide policy.

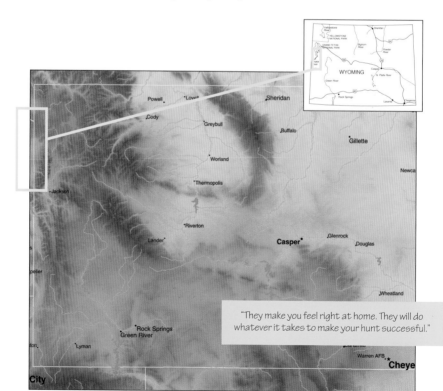

"They make you feel right at home. They will do whatever it takes to make your hunt successful."

# Hidden Hollow Hideaway

## Kelly and Jill Flynn

Box 233 • Townsend, MT 59644
ph. (406) 266-3322

"I enjoyed what has to be the one of the most delightful, enchanting, picturesque and successful Elk and Deer hunts in the United States." This quote certainly describes Hidden Hollow Hideaway.

For hunters looking for a great <u>combination</u> deer and elk hunt, the Hideaway offers a wonderful opportunity. With more than 20 years in the same area, the Hideaway team hunts more than 20,000 acres of private ranch land in conjunction with a proposed wilderness area. In 1994, one of the hunters harvested a whitetail buck that was a Safari Club world record.

In the past 10 years archery and rifle hunters have enjoyed a better than 50% success on 4 pt., 5 pt., and 6 pt. bull elk.

The Hideaway offers the hunt of a lifetime.

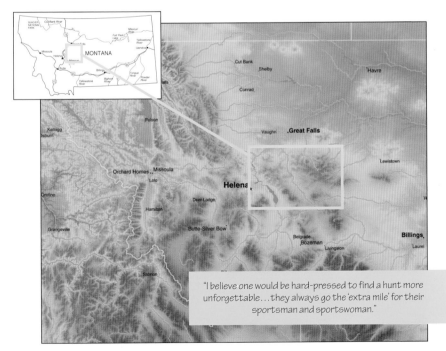

"I believe one would be hard-pressed to find a hunt more unforgettable...they always go the 'extra mile' for their sportsman and sportswoman."

# Horse Creek Outfitters

**Jim Thomas - Ric Trusnovec**

P.O. Box 950 • Challis, ID 83226

ph: J.Thomas(208) 879-5400 • R.Trusnovec (208) 879-4477

Horse Creek Outfitters is a full time, year around operation, and has been in business for 5 years.

We offer spring Bear hunting, summer family pack trips into high alpine lakes, fishing and sight-seeing, fall Elk and Deer hunts, and Lions in the winter. Our wilderness archery and rifle hunts are second to none. With three Pope & Young bulls taken the last three seasons and some fine rifle bulls from September through November. We operate three camps, a drive-in base camp and two pack-in camps personally run by the owner in each camp. Our wall tents are equipped with cots, foamies, lanterns and wood stoves.

You will find our personnel top notch, from guides and wranglers, to cooks that make home-style meals.

Your enjoyment and safety along with our hospitality is our goal.

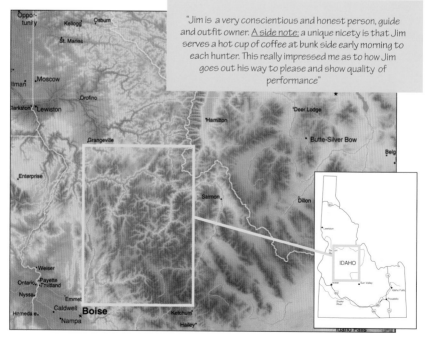

"Jim is a very conscientious and honest person, guide and outfit owner. A side note: a unique nicety is that Jim serves a hot cup of coffee at bunk side early morning to each hunter. This really impressed me as to how Jim goes out his way to please and show quality of performance"

# JM Bar Outfitters

## Jeff and Maria Freeman

23945 Bonita Road • Clinton, MT 59825
ph. (406) 825-3230 • fax (406) 825-3050

We have been providing outdoor experience for sportsman and vacationers since 1975.

We are located on Rock Creek, a blue ribbon trout stream, in the Long John Mountain Range, 30 miles east of Missoula, Montana.

We operate a full-time, year-round family outfitting business. There is abundant wildlife in the surrounding mountain including a large wild sheep population.

We aim to give you as much information about our hunt as possible, and we always enjoy talking to a fellow hunter.

Feel free to call us anytime.

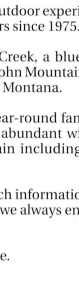

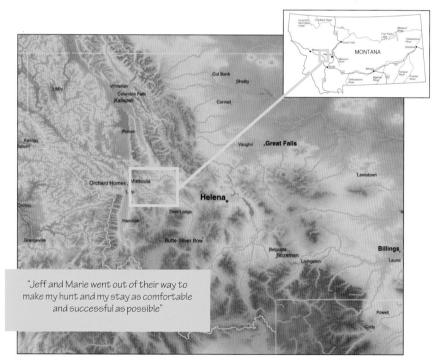

"Jeff and Marie went out of their way to make my hunt and my stay as comfortable and successful as possible"

# John Henry Lee Outfitters, Inc.

**John Lee**

Box 8368 • Jackson, WY 83002

ph. (307) 733-9441 or (800) 3-JACKSON

Quality guided pack-in horseback hunts in the Teton Wilderness area, below Yellowstone Park. Camp is located 16 miles into the wilderness area.

Hunting for elk, deer, moose, sheep and bear. Also hunting late season elk migrating from Yellowstone Park to Jackson Hole. These hunts are based from the town of Jackson and hunting is done in the Teton National Park. Archery hunts are done in the wilderness camp. We also offer summer pack-in flyfishing trips and scenic pack trips.

Friendly professional guides, great meals, gentle horses. Outfitter has 14 years guiding experience in these areas.

For a free color brochure call or write.

"What John Lee tells you is what John Lee does!!"

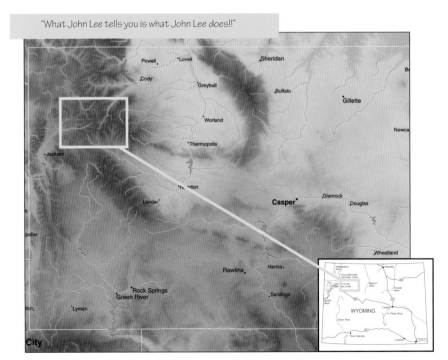

# K Bar Z Guest Ranch and Outfitters

**Dave Segall and Dawna Barnett**

P.O. Box 2167 • Cody, WY 82414

ph. (307) 587-4410 • fax (307) 527-4605

K Bar Z is a family-owned operation nestled in the heart of the Rockies in Northwest Wyoming. They have two wilderness camps and a comfortable lodge located in the Shoshone National Forest.

Our guides specialize in providing the type of hunt you want and will work hard to find the game you are looking for. Our hunt area is located just east of Yellowstone Park and is a major migration route for elk, mule deer and bighorn sheep.

This is some of the most rugged and wild country in the lower 48 states. With the top-notch guides at the K Bar Z, you could have the opportunity to bag the big one of a lifetime.

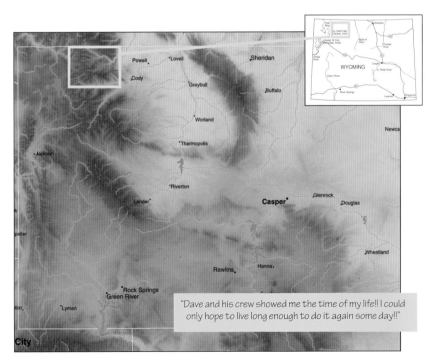

"Dave and his crew showed me the time of my life!! I could only hope to live long enough to do it again some day!!"

# Kibler Outfitting

**Myron and Mary Beth Kibler**

Box A-6 • Sand Spring, MT 59077

ph. (406) 557-2503

Our hunting areas are located 26 miles south of Sand Spring Montana. We hunt both private and BLM lands depending on the species, for a total of approximately 45,000 acres.

The limits we place upon ourselves keep the quality and quantity of our game superb. Our specialized service to our clients make return business such that we do not do paid advertising. Word of mouth advertising has served us well, having only 25-30 hunters per year. This keeps our attitude fresh and makes your vacation a very special one.

It would be our pleasure to have you and your friends hunt with us!

If you have any questions, please feel welcome to contact us at anytime.

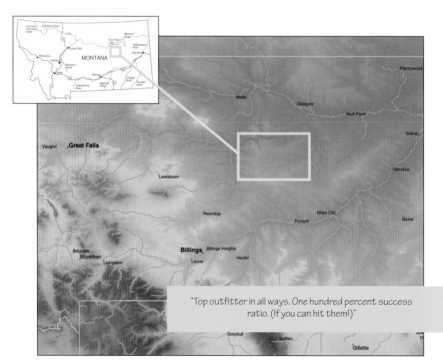

> "Top outfitter in all ways. One hundred percent success ratio. (If you can hit them!)"

# Lakeview Resort & Outfitters

**Dan Murphy**

P.O. Box 1000 • Lake City, CO 81235

phone: 800-456-0170 • (970) 944-2401 • fax:(970) 641-5952 • Lic. # 939

Our 36 years' of combined guide experience in the field provides a hunt that sells itself with limited hunters and a high number of trophy deer, new jeeps and fully-equipped camps.

Our wilderness area and horse camps are top quality.

Each archery, muzzleloader or rifle combo deer and elk hunt are limited to four-to-six hunters with three guided hunts per season.

These small camps allow time for personal treatment and room to move.

"We're in the business of making memories."

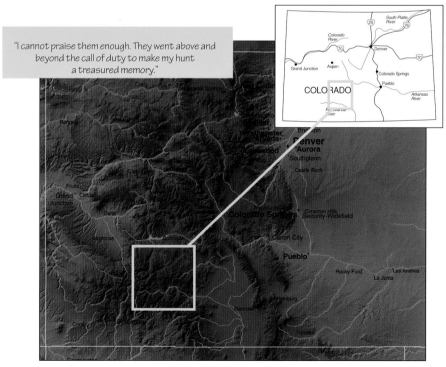

"I cannot praise them enough. They went above and beyond the call of duty to make my hunt a treasured memory."

# Lightning Creek Ranch

**Jim Werner**
1713 Walker Creek Rd. • Douglas, WY 82633
ph. (307) 358-2633

Our hunts are run on our family-owned ranches and hunters stay right in the ranch houses. With only six-to-eight hunters at a time on our 12,000-acre ranch, this makes for a good hunt with a personal touch.

The September bow hunts for antelope have averaged better than 85% success in the last ten years with 65% of the trophies making Pope and Young. Rifle deer and antelope hunts are in the first three weeks of October.

These hunts are by 4x4 spotting, then stalking by foot. Rifle elk hunts are in November.

If you are looking for a hunt with a small group and a personal touch, give us a try.

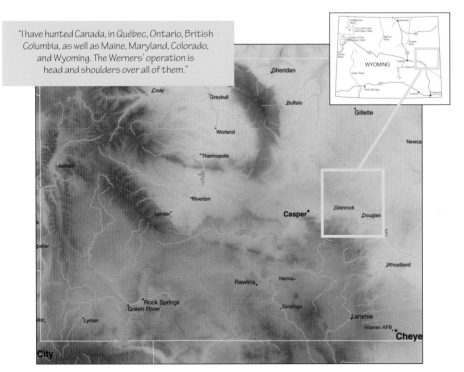

"I have hunted Canada, in Québec, Ontario, British Columbia, as well as Maine, Maryland, Colorado, and Wyoming. The Werners' operation is head and shoulders over all of them."

# Lone Tom Outfitting

## Paul Janke

12888 County Road 8 • Meeker, CO 81641
phone: (970) 878-5122 • Lic. #284

I offer fully-guided hunts or drop-camps for elk. They are all tent camps and pack-in horseback.

I hunt all archery, muzzleloader and rifle seasons. All camps are located in the Flattops Wilderness area.

Mountain Lion hunts are conducted from my lodge. I use 4-wheel drive and snowmobiles. Rooms and meals are included.

I have had 100% success for eight years.

Summer wilderness horseback trips are also available.

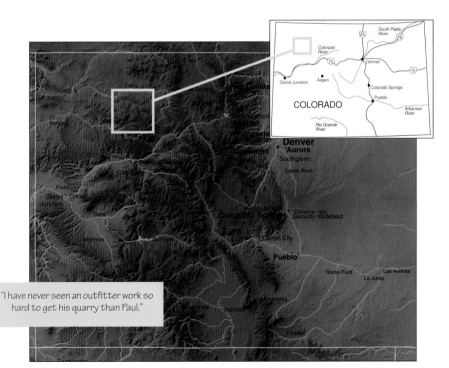

"I have never seen an outfitter work so hard to get his quarry than Paul."

# Lone Tree Outfitting

**Larry Pendleton**
1531 Iron Cap Rd. • Stevensville, MT 59870
ph. (406) 777-3906

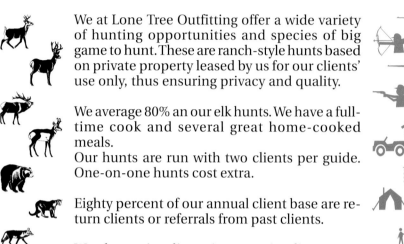

We at Lone Tree Outfitting offer a wide variety of hunting opportunities and species of big game to hunt. These are ranch-style hunts based on private property leased by us for our clients' use only, thus ensuring privacy and quality.

We average 80% an our elk hunts. We have a full-time cook and several great home-cooked meals.
Our hunts are run with two clients per guide. One-on-one hunts cost extra.

Eighty percent of our annual client base are return clients or referrals from past clients.

We also assist clients in procuring licenses to hunt with us.

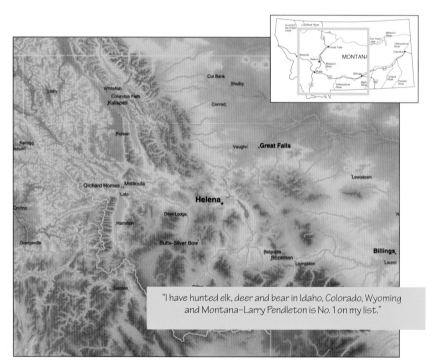

"I have hunted elk, deer and bear in Idaho, Colorado, Wyoming and Montana–Larry Pendleton is No. 1 on my list."

# Love Bros. & Lee, Ltd.

**Ron Fleming**
R.R. #1 Kispiox Road, Site N • Hazelton, B.C., Canada V0J 1Y0
phone: (250) 842-6350

We specialize in combination hunts for mountain goat, mountain caribou, moose, grizzly, black bear and wolf — with bow or rifle. With five camps on lakes and rivers in 2,500-square miles of pristine wilderness, we have exclusive guiding rights to some of the best hunting and fishing in Northern British Columbia.

We provide guides, food, cooks, boats, motor, cabins, charter floatplanes trips and complete field care of trophies. Catering to small groups of four guests at a time, we offer excellent homecooked meals and professional guide service with a personal touch.

Our commitment to excellence and hunting ethics assures each guest a memorable trip.

"Nothing I could say could ever come close to the great experience I had with this outfit and guide. It's like jumping from planes into combat - you have to try it!!"

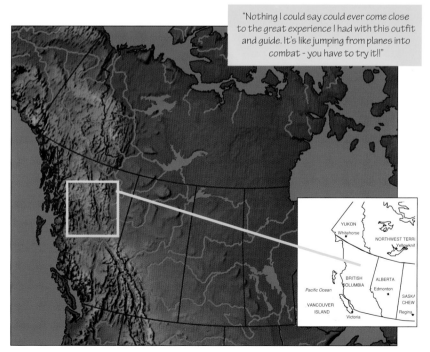

# Mitchell Outfitting

## Floyd Mitchell

PO Box 228 • Broadus, MT 59317
ph. (406) 436-2522 • Camp (406) 427-5810

Floyd Mitchell, owner of Mitchell Outfitting, has been in the Outfitting business for 18 years.

We specialize in mule deer, whitetail, antelope, prairie dogs, varmint calling, turkey, upland game birds and family vacation packages. Our guided hunts take place on beautiful and scenic private ranches in Powder River and Carter counties. We have modern facilities with showers, and home-cooked meals provided.

We take pride in offering exceptional hunting with experienced guides.

You will not find a better average of good bucks taken right here in Eastern Montana.

We guarantee you will be more than pleased, not only with the hunting, but with all aspects of our service.

"Floyd Mitchell and his guide are of the quality that makes them the best in the business. The hunting cabin is rustic, but hell, that makes it all for the better."

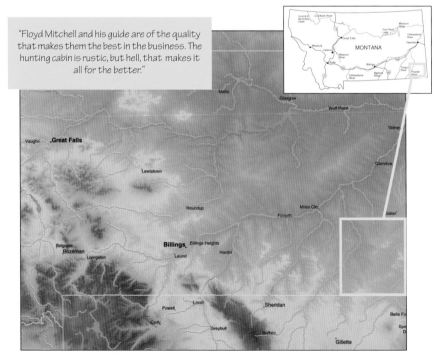

# Moose Valley Outfitters

## Ronald Steffey

General Delivery • Germansen Landing, B.C., Canada V0J 1T0
Radio phone: Vancouver Operator N50052, Channel 8

Our guiding territory is located in the rugged mountains of Northern British Columbia and is extremely remote with spectacular, breathtaking scenery, and trophy-class game.

We live in our guiding area year-round and recently completed an octagon log lodge. All of our hunting camps have comfortable log cabins. In order to maintain the wilderness atmosphere and assure your privacy, we specialize in small groups or families. Surround yourself in the majestic beauty of snowcapped mountains, meadows blanketed with wildflowers, beautiful glacier-fed lakes, and crystal-clear streams.

Hunt trophy-class game in their natural habitat in pristine wilderness.

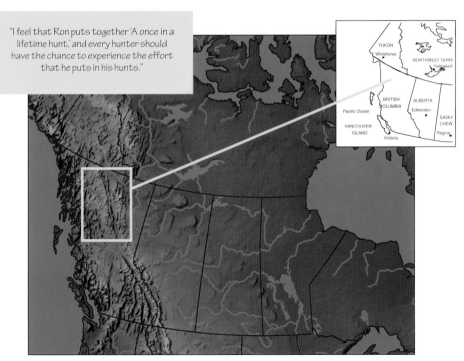

"I feel that Ron puts together 'A once in a lifetime hunt,' and every hunter should have the chance to experience the effort that he puts in his hunts."

# P Cross Bar Ranch

**Marion and Mary Scott**

8585 North Highway 14 -16 • Gillette, WY 82716

ph. (307) 682-3994 • fax (307) 682-3684

Safari Club International's 1993 North American Professional Hunter's of the Year, Marion and Mary Scott have been serving the hunting public for almost 45 years.

We work hard to make every hunt a quality experience. Our experienced guides cover 200,000 acres of private ranches located in beautiful wildlife-filled Northeast Wyoming.

Family hunts, youth hunts, handicapped hunts and alternative weapon hunts are encouraged and are very successful.

With the able help of longtime guides such as Dudley Mackey, Mick Shober and Dan Hunsaker, Marion and Mary have produced many outstanding-award winning trophies for their clients.

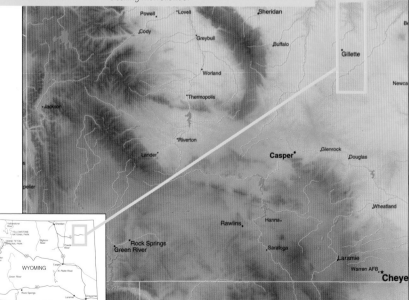

"An excellent operation, run very well by knowledgeable, honest, caring individuals with vast experience regarding games, area, and most importantly, dealing with clients."

# Phil's Bowhunting Adventures

**Phil Phillips**

P.O. Box 786 • Montrose, CO 81402

phone/fax: (970) 249-8068 • Lic. #977

Here at Phil's Bowhunting Adventures, we specialize in archery antelope hunts. We hunt Northwest Colorado near Maybell on 40,000-plus deeded acres. We work under a Ranching for Wildlife Program, which guarantees hunters a tag without a draw. In the past six years we have 100% shooting opportunities and more than 90% success with 65% record book animals.

After eight years of trophy management our number of trophy animals just keeps getting better.

Well known, Chuck Adams has hunted with us the past six years and is booked through the year 2000. We have been in business 15 years. We also offer mule deer, elk and mountain lion hunts. We look forward to hunting with you.

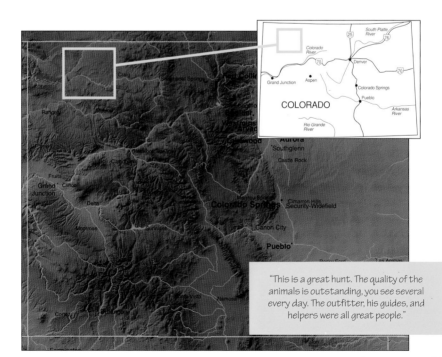

"This is a great hunt. The quality of the animals is outstanding, you see several every day. The outfitter, his guides, and helpers were all great people."

# Pusch Ridge Outfitters

**Kirk and Roxane Kelso**

10260 N. Hardage Lane • Oro Valley, AZ 85737

phone: (520) 544-0954

Kirk Kelso of Pusch Ridge Outfitters is noted as one of the premier outfitters in the country for Coues' whitetail.

The hunt area has produced some of the top heads in Boone & Crockett, Safari Club International, Pope & Young and the Longhunter Record Books. Hunters take a number of bucks scoring 100-plus points every year, including a buck in 1995 that scored 121 points.

The Kelsos are noted for their successful antelope, elk, desert bighorn sheep, Rocky Mountain bighorn, desert mule deer and javelina hunts. Antelope and elk are hunted in Arizona and New Mexico with high-scoring trophies taken every year.

Their New Mexico antelope lease produced four B&C heads out of eight hunts in 1995.

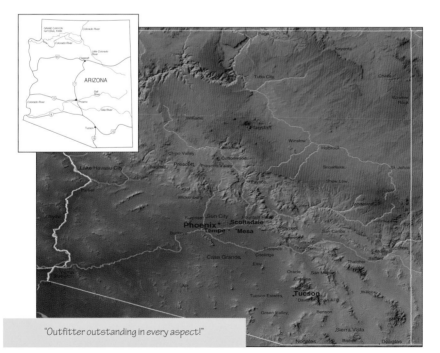

*"Outfitter outstanding in every aspect!"*

# Ramshorn Outfitters

## Audie and Vivianne Anderson

P.O. Box 662 • Townsend, MT 59644
ph. (406) 266-3095

Ramshorn Outfitters offers a large variety of hunts to suit most hunters and their personal goals.

You can hunt high alpine areas for elk or lower more varying terrain for mule deer or whitetail deer or test your stalking skills against a sharp-eyed antelope. Vivianne and I pride ourselves in providing a quality trip and polished camp. Food and accommodation are top-notch.

We specialize in quality trips and I personally believe every hunting trip should be treated as a once-in-a-lifetime experience; let us make yours a great one.

Our high rate of repeat clients says it all!

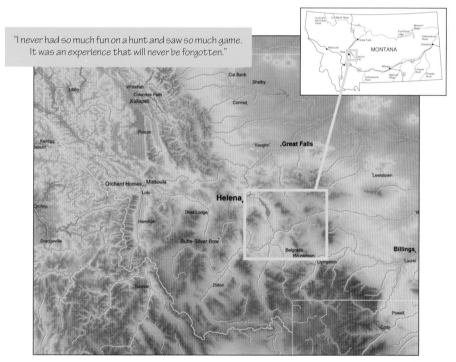

"I never had so much fun on a hunt and saw so much game. It was an experience that will never be forgotten."

# Red Desert Adventures

**Vic R. Dana**

PO Box 2324 • Rock Springs, WY 82902-2324
ph. (307) 362-8056

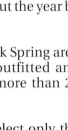

I am proud to offer the serious hunter some of the finest pronghorn antelope, mule deer, elk, and Shiras moose in Wyoming today. I feel I can provide the best hunting available because I extensively scout my areas throughout the year by taking my own personal survey.

I am a lifetime resident of the Rock Spring area of Southwest Wyoming. I have outfitted and personally hunted this area for more than 25 years.

This experience enables me to select only the best areas for my clients and give them the best possible chances for success.

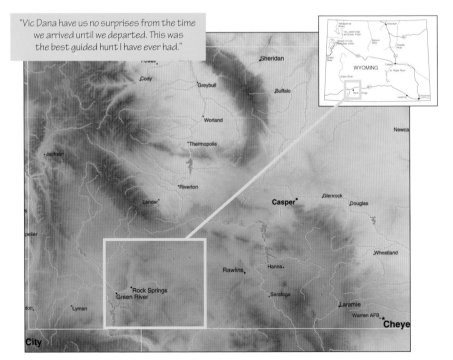

"Vic Dana have us no surprises from the time we arrived until we departed. This was the best guided hunt I have ever had."

# Renshaw Outfitting, Inc.

**Jim Renshaw**
PO Box 1165 • Kamiah, ID 83536-1165
ph. (208) 935-0726 • (926) 4520 • (800) 452-2567

"Go with the best and most experienced outfitter in the state of Idaho."

Licensed and bonded the longest in Idaho. Offering the following fully-guided deluxe hunts: spring black bear (different color phases) in May and June; deluxe fall bugle archery elk hunts (tree stand available); deluxe guided rifle elk hunts; and late fall whitetail hunts on private land in November.

All hunts are fully guided and everything is furnished except personal gear and licenses. If you book an hunt early, the license and tags can be purchased from Idaho's outfitter set-aside pool. Facilities are deluxe tent camps with floored tents, wood heat, running water, hot showers, and lights. We serve home style meals.

Please call for further information, or to book a hunt.

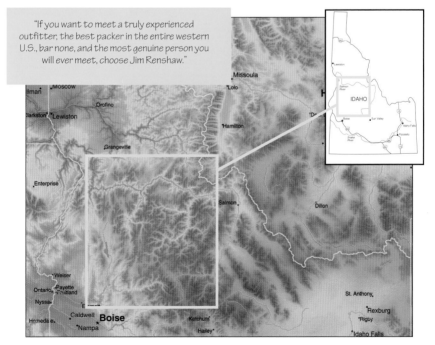

"If you want to meet a truly experienced outfitter, the best packer in the entire western U.S., bar none, and the most genuine person you will ever meet, choose Jim Renshaw."

# Rick Wemple Outfitting

**Rick Wemple**
1765 Pleasant View Drive • Victor, MT 59875
ph. (406) 642-3869

Extreme hunts for trophies, that is what I offer. Only the fit need apply.

I will hunt my hunters until they either kill or quit. I provide all the equipment, food and transportation of hunters and game. I offer hunts that are physical and in any kind of weather. Overnight in the woods, on the trail of trophies means we take what we need to survive and continue hunting the next day.

I have spent my entire life in Western Montana and in the Selway Wilderness area. I started guiding in 1974 and got my outfitter license in 1982. All I know is hunting, guiding and outfitting. I know my area and game. I try as hard as possible to get my clients the game they seek. My hunts are tailored and priced for the hunters who are looking for true fair chase trophies in Idaho or Montana.

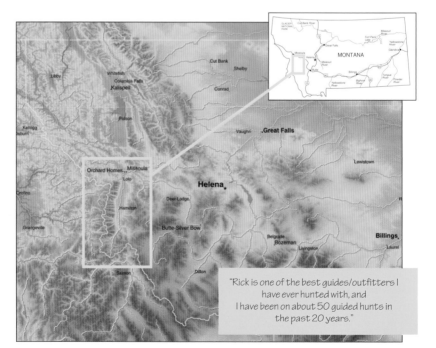

"Rick is one of the best guides/outfitters I have ever hunted with, and I have been on about 50 guided hunts in the past 20 years."

# River S Enterprises

## Mike and Debbie Schwiebert

P.O. Box 286 • Santa Margerita, CA 93453
phone: (805) 466-7741 • fax: (805) 466-9903
cellular: (805) 440-0109

All hunts are conducted on quality, well-managed private concessions in California and Wyoming under exclusive leases.

Meals are excellently prepared, nutritious and plentiful. Hunts are conducted with one guide for two hunters.

Guides are experienced professionals who are dedicated to the client's success. Mike and Debbie are dedicated to providing the finest quality outdoor experience possible. It is their policy to provide each client with a safe, successful and enjoyable outdoor experience.

They put forth 100% to meet these objectives. "Should a client feel that we have not fulfilled our efforts, we will refund 100% of the cost."

"I can't say enough good things about Mike Schwiebert and his team. They are knowledgeable, reliable, dedicated and nice people. I felt welcome and part of the group immediately."

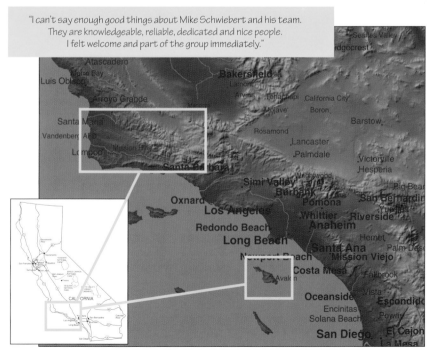

# R.L. Sourbrine Outfitters and Sons

## Richard Sourbrine
2019 Meridian Road • Victor, MT 59875
ph. (406) 642-3251

Family-owned and operated with 16 years in the business.

We offer hunts for elk, deer, black bear, goat, sheep, moose in the heart of the Bitteroot Valley. Day hunts, accommodations included. Guest cabin. Four hunters to a party.

Private ground and national forest land. Transportation to and from Missoula airport included. Local meat processing available.

Some of the best taxidermists are in the area. Clients should make reservations January of the year they want to hunt. Private ranch available for elk, mule deer and buffalo.

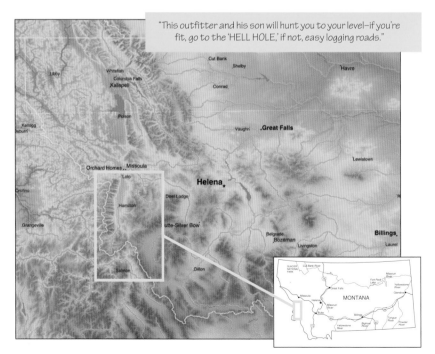

"This outfitter and his son will hunt you to your level–if you're fit, go to the 'HELL HOLE,' if not, easy logging roads."

# S&W Outfitters

**Brad Hanzel**

PO Box 160520 • Big Sky, MT 59716
ph.(406) 995-2658 • Sept.-Nov (406) 538-4864

**Howard Seymour**

PO Box 76 • Sandy Creek, NY 13145
ph.(315) 387-5806 • Sept.-Nov. (406) 538-4864

S&W Outfitters was established in 1981 with the idea of treating clients with the same consideration and respect that we would like if in their place.

Our goal is to provide our clients with a first-class hunt and very memorable experience, to be remembered long after their trophy mounts have faded and lost their splendor.

We would like to express our gratitude for your interest in S&W Outfitters.

We hope you will join us next year for the hunt of your dreams.

Please call us to discuss any questions you may have about our hunts.

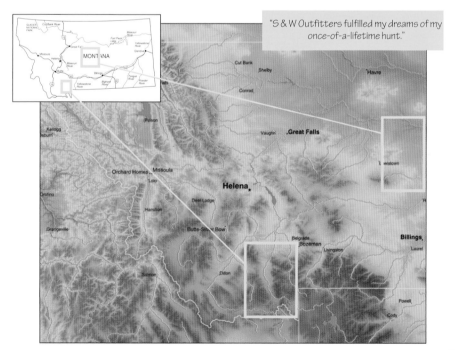

"S & W Outfitters fulfilled my dreams of my once-of-a-lifetime hunt."

# Samuelson Outfitters

**Dick and Cathy Samuelson**
P.O. Box 868 • Fraser, CO 80442
ph. (970) 726-8221 • Lic. #721

Samuelson Outfitters, a family business, has operated for more than 25 years in the Troublesome Basin.

It is one of the premiere elk hunting areas in Colorado and is noted for its considerable percentage of large bulls and abundance of wildlife. It is an area that one will remember for years to come and a place to which our family has grown very attached.

We offer fully-guided elk and mule deer hunts, drop-camps and pack service for archery, muzzleloader and rifle hunts. We also offer summer horsepack trips.

"The outfitters equipment and facilities are second to none–real comfort in a wilderness camp–they are attentive to their hunters needs and comfort."

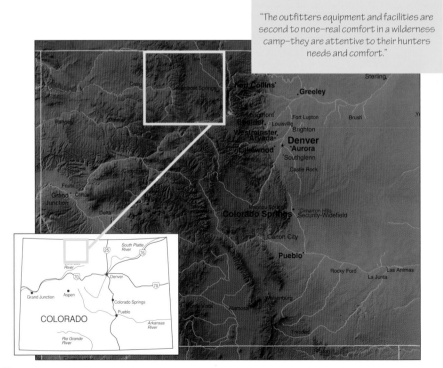

# San Juan Outfitting, LLC

**Tom and Cheri Van Soelen**
186 C.R. 228 • Durango, CO 81301
ph. (970) 259-6259 • fax (970) 259-2652
email: sjo@frontier.net • Lic. #997

San Juan Outfitting (SJO) offers spring, summer and fall pack trips for a wide variety of services.

We are a full-time family-owned and operated outfitting company. Our permits are in the Weminuche Wilderness, Piedra area and San Juan National Forest. SJO offers fully-guided, semi-guided and drop-camps for rifle, archery, and muzzleloader hunters.

All camps are restricted to foot and horseback travel only. We believe in offering only high-quality hunts to a few hunters each year.

Enjoying not only the hunt, but all of God's country.

"Showed me an incredible knowledge of the area and was able to put me <u>directly</u> on big game multiple times…"

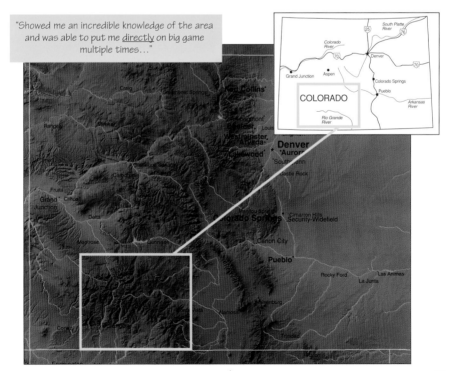

# Spadafora Ranch Lodge

**Roger Cesario**

P.O. Box 1116 • Crested Butte, CO 81224
Home (970) 349-9836 • Ranch (970) 929-5201 • Lic. #711

Spadafora Ranch Lodge is located in Gunnison County and surrounded by Gunnison National Forest.

The ranch has been owned by the same family since 1929, and has had a hunting operation since early 1960s. Roger Cesario has been running the hunting operation as an outfitter since 1982 and received the Colorado Good Sportsman Award in 1992. Hunting is done from the lodge with jeeps to the hunting areas and on foot. Horses are utilized to pack the game.

We hunt both private land and Gunnison National Forest. Elk numbers of mature bulls on the ranch are excellent and mule deer number are also good.

The lodge is comfortable with hot showers, rooms for every two hunters, heat in the room, full kitchen and excellent elk hunting from the front door.

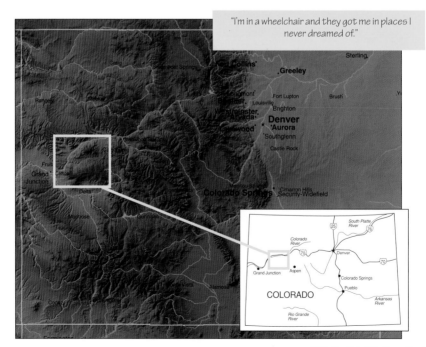

"I'm in a wheelchair and they got me in places I never dreamed of."

# Stricker Outfitting, Ltd.

## Charlie Stricker

Box 5963 • Whitehorse, Yukon., Canada, Y1A 5L7
phone/fax: (403) 633-3366

We offer mighty bucks from the mighty Peace River Country of Alberta.

This is the most remote whitetail deer area available with nil or minimal hunting pressure. Hunters are positioned in prime tree stands in early morning before daylight and again in late evening. The stands are heated and positioned over active scrapes and rubs. During the day, we do drives or pushes. The guide will walk through the bush and drive the deer past the hunter. There is also an opportunity to take a coyote or wolf on these hunts.

We offer a bow and arrow bighorn sheep hunt out of Canmore, Alberta. On this hunt, when you step out of your tent, you're hunting.

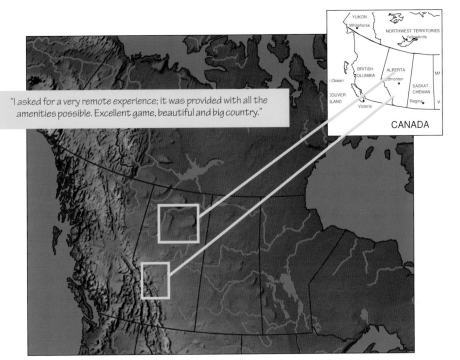

"I asked for a very remote experience; it was provided with all the amenities possible. Excellent game, beautiful and big country."

# Swift Creek Outfitters

## B.J. and Vicki Hill

PO Box 1472 • Afton, WY 83110

ph. (307) 886-5470

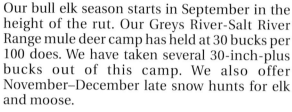

Swift Creek Outfitters is owned by the Hill family in Afton, Wyoming. Our Jackson Hole elk camp has, in the past few years, held at 26 bulls per 100 cows postseason count.

Our bull elk season starts in September in the height of the rut. Our Greys River-Salt River Range mule deer camp has held at 30 bucks per 100 does. We have taken several 30-inch-plus bucks out of this camp. We also offer November–December late snow hunts for elk and moose.

We pack high-quality binoculars and hunt hard for our clients.

Our reputation is very important to us. A free color brochure is available on request.

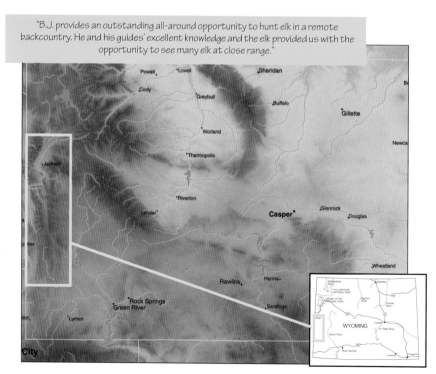

"B.J. provides an outstanding all-around opportunity to hunt elk in a remote backcountry. He and his guides' excellent knowledge and the elk provided us with the opportunity to see many elk at close range."

# T Lazy T Outfitters

## Tom Toolson Outfitters
Box 1288 • Jackson Hole, WY 83001
ph. (307) 733-4481

T Lazy T Outfitters is family-operated, and has been doing business for the past 29 years.

With approximately 80 hunting days, a maximum of 20 hunters, and one of the largest area authorizations in Northwest Wyoming (which enables us to move with the game), we are able to specialize your hunt. We spike camp for sheep and moose.

Outfitting and guiding year-round is my only business. Year-end reports furnished upon request.

Consistently high harvest is my personal guarantee for a rewarding hunt.

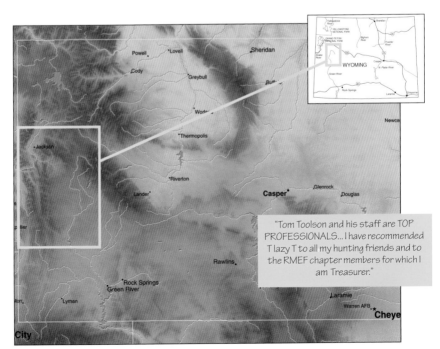

"Tom Toolson and his staff are TOP PROFESSIONALS... I have recommended T lazy T to all my hunting friends and to the RMEF chapter members for which I am Treasurer."

# Terrero General Store and Riding Stables, Inc.

**Huie Ley**

P.O. Box 12 • Terrero, NM 87573

ph. (505) 757-6193

This is a family-owned and operated business. My father, Happy Ley, started the business working for a guest ranch at Cowels in 1927.

We outfit into the Santa Fe National Forest and the Pecos Wilderness. The Wilderness encompasses approximately 230,000 acres which, in turn, is surrounded by approximately 300,000 acres of national forest. The Pecos Wilderness is located in both Carson and Santa Fe national forests. Elevation runs from 6,000 feet in the foothills to over 13,000 feet at the summit of Truchas Peak.

Primitive conditions are preserved for the use, enjoyment and spiritual refreshment of the people. For more information give us a call.

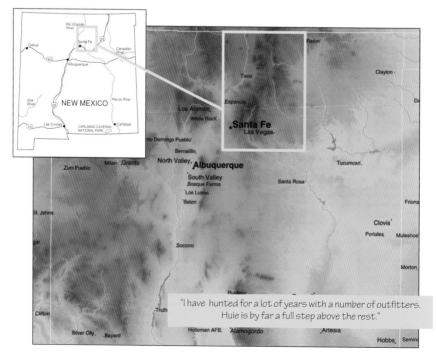

"I have hunted for a lot of years with a number of outfitters. Huie is by far a full step above the rest."

# Timberline Outfitters

### Perry and Brenda Hunsaker

19831 E. Warner Rd. • Higley, AZ 85236
phone: (505) 547-2413 • (602) 988-9654

All clients are guided one-on-one unless otherwise arranged. Our guides are seasoned hunters and know what it takes to get you on your trophy.

It's no secret that the areas we hunt are considered by most experts the best in North America. New Mexico and Arizona are the hot spots. If your dream is a trophy-class animal, you are in the right spot.

Our meals consist of roast beef and turkey with all the trimmings. You will not go hungry in this camp. Camps range from ranch headquarters with individually-heated rooms to comfortable tent camps.

We want your trip to be a success. You have my word we will do our best so that your stay will be a memorable and rewarding experience.

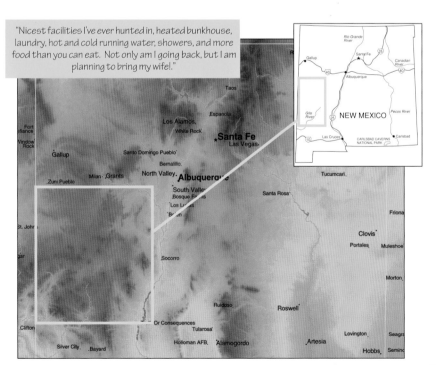

"Nicest facilities I've ever hunted in, heated bunkhouse, laundry, hot and cold running water, showers, and more food than you can eat. Not only am I going back, but I am planning to bring my wife!."

# Tom Scott Outfitting

**Tom Scott**
Box 1122 • Westlock, Alberta, Canada T0G 2L0
phone/fax: (403) 349-3931

Tom Scott Outfitting is a small, very personalized operation with the outfitter on site and a maximum of four clients per six-day hunt.

We access fairly remote areas of Northern Alberta for moose, mule deer and bear, mainly by ATV. Camp accommodations consist of tents with heaters, cots with mattresses and good home cooked meals.

Whitetail deer are hunted from my home in farming country in North Central Alberta.

Highly experienced guides (whitetail, one-on-one, others two-on-one) work hard to show clients good animals with excellent success rates.

Come as a client, go home as a friend.

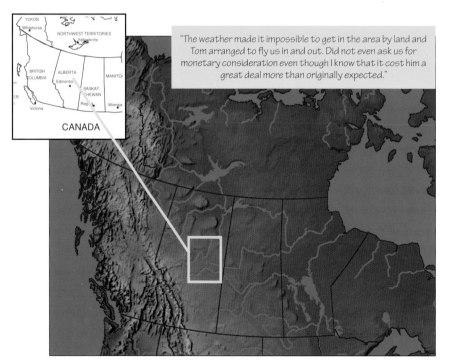

"The weather made it impossible to get in the area by land and Tom arranged to fly us in and out. Did not even ask us for monetary consideration even though I know that it cost him a great deal more than originally expected."

# Triangle C Ranch

**Cameron Garnick**
3737 US Highway 26 • Dubois, WY 82513
ph. (307) 455-2225 • fax (307) 455-2031

We are a fair chase outfit, hunting big bulls in Jackson Hole and Shosohone National Forest.

We specialize in early archery hunts and sheep hunt on the headwaters of Yellowstone River.

We are a family-run operation, and the outfitter is in camp.

Our guides have worked with us for years and have the country in their bones.

We pride ourselves in good beds, great food and the best company.

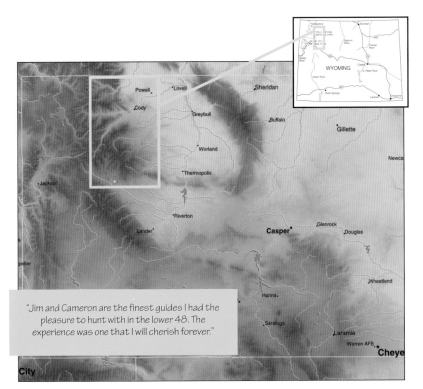

"Jim and Cameron are the finest guides I had the pleasure to hunt with in the lower 48. The experience was one that I will cherish forever."

# Twin Pine Ranch

**Larry and Peg Gerke**
644 Harris Park Rd. •Wheatland, WY 82201
ph. (307) 322-2485

The Twin Pine Ranch, a private cattle ranch in beautiful mountain surroundings, has been offering a guided hunting program since 1984 with very high hunter success rates.

As we guide on our 13,000 acres of private land only, the game is big and plentiful and you are assured of exclusive hunting, using 4-wheel drive vehicles.

We work hard to provide excellent guiding service, top-notch meals and clean comfortable lodging.

Our many returning hunters seem to feel at home where our friendly and caring program does make a difference.

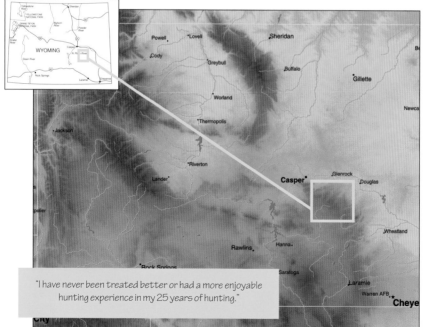

"I have never been treated better or had a more enjoyable hunting experience in my 25 years of hunting."

# Western Guiding Service

**Greg, Dave and Betty Molloy**

Box 191 • Empress, Alberta, Canada T0J 1EO

phone: (403) 565-3775 • (403) 676-3300

Western Guiding Service is a family-run business specializing in trophy mule deer hunts for rifle and bow in Southeastern Alberta in four wildlife management units, which have been on resident draw since 1989.

This unique area has repeatedly provided clients with world-class mule deer each year.

Bow hunts are conducted on both the South Saskatchewan and Red Deer Rivers by jet and conventional boats.

Dave or Greg would like to talk to you about a mule deer hunt. Please call and get on our list for a hunt to remember.

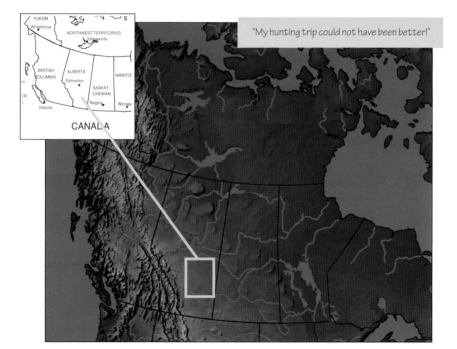

"My hunting trip could not have been better!"

# Western Wyoming Trophy Hunts

**Levi Lozier**

Box 100 • Cora, WY 82925

ph. (800) 822-8466 • (307) 367-4868 • fax (307) 367-6260

Come join Levi Lozier, a fifth generation outfitter, and his experienced crew for some of the finest elk, mule deer, antelope, bighorn sheep and Shiras moose hunting in Wyoming.

We are located on the west slope of the Wind River Mountain Range. First-class service and accommodations coupled with 45 years of quality hunting and excellent success are the pride of Western Wyoming Trophy Hunts.

One of only a few places in the Western U.S. where you can hunt elk with a rifle (Sept. 20) while the elk are bugling and in the heat of the rut.

Call now for more information.

"This is a family operation and they take great pride in that. ... I have hunted others when I have not drawn. But they do not compare with this outfitter."

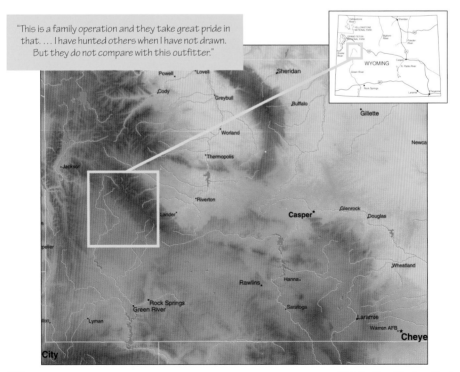

# White Tail Ranch/WTR Outfitters, Inc.

**Jack and Karen Hooker**

520 Cooper Lake Rd. • Ovando, MT 59854

ph. (888)WTR-5666 • (406) 793-5666

email: wtroutfitters@montana.com • www.recworld.com/wtro

White Tail Ranch Outfitters has been specializing in summer wilderness education pack trips and big game hunting since 1940.

Over the years our main hunt schedule has consisted of guided parties. We provide a deluxe camp with everything furnished. We also provide outfitted drop camp service. Our camps are between 9 and 21 miles, by horse and packstring from our trailhead.

We have a high rate of success with the percentage of opportunities being even higher.

We are in Montana to service our guest from far and wide.

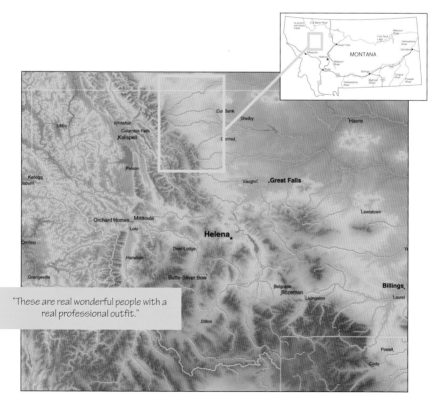

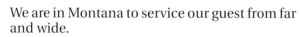

"These are real wonderful people with a real professional outfit."

# Wild West Outfitters

**Michael A. Goyins**
2595 York Rd. • Helena, MT 59601
ph. (406) 449-6549

Wild West Outfitters offers some of the finest elk, deer and bear hunting in the state of Montana. Specializing in elk archery hunts, our goal is to be the best at what we do.

All hunting is done on private land. The animals are wild and free, each presenting a unique hunting challenge.

Wild West Outfitters offers not only memorable hunts, but also an opportunity to experience Montana's high-mountain beauty and develop friendships that will last a lifetime.

We guarantee an adventure you won't soon forget.

"I have hunted all over US and Canada and Wild West Outfitters is by far top-notch. I can't say enough good things about Mike Goyins."

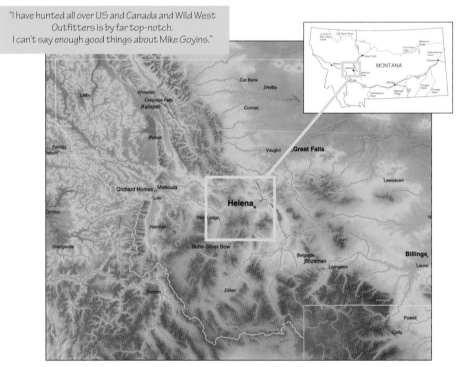

# Top Rated Bird Hunting

## Guides and Outfitters

# Eagle Nest Lodge & Outfitters

**Keith Kelly**

P.O. Box 509 • Hardin, MT 59034
phone: (406) 665-3711 • fax: (406) 665-3712

Eagle Nest, secluded on the banks of the Bighorn River, was the first in the world to receive the Orvis endorsement for excellence in wing-shooting and service.

The lodging and dining are synonymous with excellence, and the hills, creeks and fields of south-central Montana provide premier habitat for some of the world's finest upland bird hunting. Pheasants, Hungarian partridge and sharptail grouse abound 35,000 acres of private land open to Eagle Nest guests. Hunts are conducted by professional guides using German shorthairs, Brittanies, and English pointers. The shooting is quite challenging but the birds are plentiful.

A family business since its conception in 1982, Eagle Nest is owned and managed by the Kellys.

"I hunted for three days and I wish I had booked a longer trip. The area is beautiful and the birds were everywhere. Eagle Nest is a first class operation all the way from the dogs, to the birds, to the food." Jack Duley in "The Bird Hunting Report"

# Echo Canyon Outfitters

## David Hampton

P.O. Box 328 • La Veta, CO 81055
phone: (800) 341-6603 • (719) 742-5524 • fax: (719) 742-5525
email: echo@rmi.net • www.guestecho.com • Lic. #1143

Echo Canyon Outfitters provides first-class trophy- quality hunts on a private ranch. Our hunters are guided one-on-one by experienced guides who are very knowledgeable of the terrain and wildlife. The hunts are extremely professional, offering quality accommodations, food, stock, and personnel.

We are active members of Rocky Mountain Elk Foundation as sponsors, donors and habitat partners. Our Long Canyon Ranch is strictly managed for wildlife habitat and trophy-class production under a conservation easement with RMEF. The outfit brings 12 years' of solid experience to our business.

We annually re-book more than 75% of our clients two years in advance. We specialize in trophy elk and mule deer, black bear, mountain lion and <u>turkey</u>.

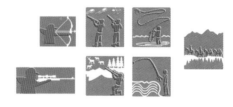

"Echo Canyon Outfitters are very professional yet they treat you like family. They go out of their way to ensure you a memorable experience."

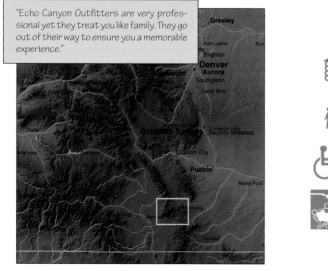

# Good's Bird Hunts/Eagle Outfitters

**Gerry Good**

P.O. Box 1042 • Ravalli, MT 59863
phone/fax: (406) 745-3491
email: sti3491@Montana.com

Good's Bird Hunts is a small central Montana company, offering first-class upland bird hunts. We provide the client with room and board, guides, dogs, transportation, and preparation of birds for shipping. Our season runs from September to mid-December, but is usually over when the weather turns bad in mid-November.

Because bird populations vary year to year, we offer different locations for lodging, from first-class motels to ranch-style accommodations where we stay on the ranch with home-cooked meals and bunkhouse beds. Most lunches are in the field.

We use Griffon pointing dogs, or you can use your dogs in partnership with ours. Groups are limited to three per guide. Our package is a four-night, three-day hunt with meals starting on the first night. Airport pickups can be arranged at Billings and Great Falls or other airports.

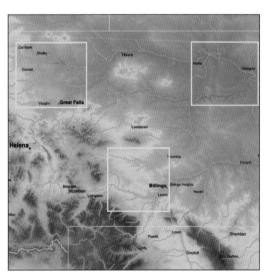

# Triple B Outfitters

**David L. Gill**

616 W. Broadway • Lewistown, MT 59457

phone: (406) 538-2177

Central Montana is known nationwide for its excellent bird hunting due to the many different and abundant species of upland game birds. Hungarian partridge, sharptail grouse, ruffed grouse, blue grouse, sage hen and pheasant make for the finest in bird hunting.

If you would like to visit Montana and take part in some of the best bird hunting anywhere, we can arrange one- to five-day hunts for up to six people at a time.

We provide full guide service, transportation, access to quality private land with excellent bird populations, dogs and lunch in the field. You provide your own lodging, breakfast and dinner.

"He (Dave Gill) is a first class person, completely honest and capable of providing a very successful and enjoyable hunt. My son and I are waterfowl guides and outfitters. We know what it takes to provide a memorable hunt and Dave gives it all." George Carr

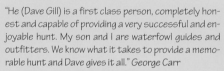

# Wapiti River Guides

**Gary Lane**

P.O. Box 1125 • Riggins, ID 83549
phone: (800) 488-9872 • (208) 628-3523 • fax: (208) 628-3523
email: wapitirg@cyberhighway.net

Float Idaho's Salmon River by driftboat for chukar hunting and steelhead fishing combination trips. Flowing through the second deepest gorge in North America, the river will introduce you to steep, rugged terrain.

After traversing the breathtaking terra firma with your dog (if you like), come back to the boats and relax with a fishing rod in your hands — that is, until a magnificent red-sided steelhead takes your line into the sky.

We place two clients per driftboat and send a baggage boat and crew ahead to secure camps, which allows us more time to hunt and fish between destinations.

Trips range from one to six days. Chukar/steelhead trips are offered only on the Salmon River. Steelhead fishing is offered on both the Salmon and Oregon's Grande Ronde River, a fly fishermen's paradise. Whitewater and scenic trips are also offered.

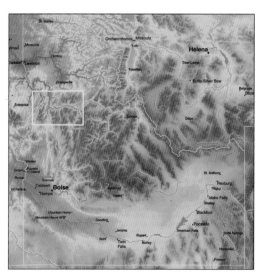

# Western Guiding Service

## Dave and Greg Molloy

Box 191 • Empress, Alberta, Canada T0J 1E0
phone/fax: (403) 565-3775

Western Guiding Service operates from a private lodge on the Alberta-Saskatchewan border. The location, licensing and bonding creates a unique opportunity to hunt Alberta and Saskatchewan for whitefront, Canada, Ross and snow geese on the same day. Also many mallard, pintail, widgeon, teal and canvasback ducks are in the area which we hunt.

Adding upland birds to the mix (sharptail grouse and Hungarian partridge) makes this an exciting hunt. From September 1-30, sandhill cranes are also hunted.

Full-service accommodations, bird cleaning and freezing space included.

"Outstanding knowledge of the area, local ranches, etc." D.C. Priest

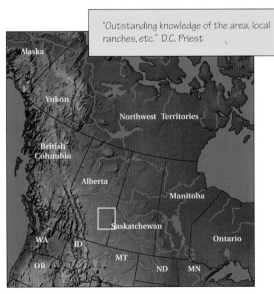

# Top Rated Fly Fishing

## Guides, Outfitters and Lodges

# Alpine Anglers Flyshop and Boulder Mountain Adventures

### Rich and Lori Cropper

310 W. Main, P.O. Box 750308 • Torrey, UT 84775
phone: (435) 425-3660 • (888) 484-3331
email: brookies@color-country.net • www.color-country.net/~brookies

Experience the flyfishing trip of a lifetime in scenic southern Utah. Brookies, cutthroat, speckle and tiger trout fill the waters of more than 80 high mountain lakes, streams and beaver ponds on beautiful Boulder Mountain.

We offer day trips and overnight flyfishing pack trips. Our flyshop will outfit you with top-of-the-line flyfishing equipment.

Friendly, knowledgeable guides provide a rewarding experience for the novice as well as the seasoned angler.

" Fishing was great...we've never experienced fishing in a float tube before. What fun we had."
Wendy and Chat Hailstone

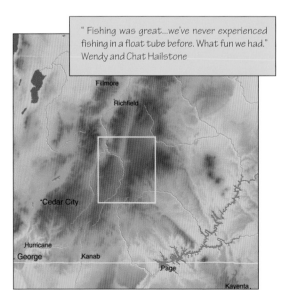

# Broken Arrow Lodge

**Erwin and Sherry Clark**

2200 Upper Ruby Rd., P.O. Box 177 • Alder, MT 59710
phone: (800) 775-2928 • phone/fax: (406) 842-5437
www.recworld.com/state/mt/hunt/broken/broken.html

With private access and minimal fishing pressure, the Ruby offers some of the finest fishing in Montana and tends to be the most popular with our guests.

The Ruby is a friendly stream, easily waded. The small streams in the backcountry are easily accessible and offer great fishing for cutthroats along with breathtaking scenery and abundant wildlife. Lake fishing on Clark Canyon provides an opportunity to catch the "big fish," rainbows and browns average 4-1/2 pounds. A short distance from the lodge, float trips on the Big Hole, Madison, Yellowstone, Beaverhead and Jefferson rivers are available on request and provide exhilarating experiences with beautiful scenery, quality fishing and the thrill of floating the river. We recommend mid-June until late September for the most rewarding fishing trip.

We offer the option to fish on your own or with a guide.

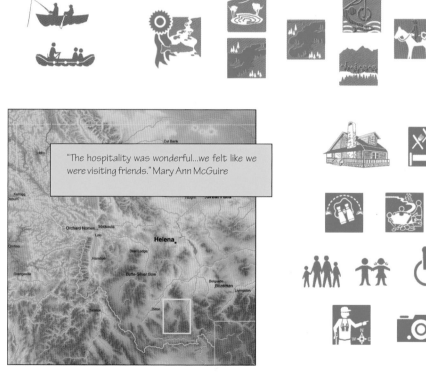

"The hospitality was wonderful...we felt like we were visiting friends." Mary Ann McGuire

# Dragonfly Anglers

## Rod and Roger Cesario

307 Elk Ave., P.O. Box 1116 • Crested Butte, CO 81224
phone: (800) 491-3079 • (970) 349-1228 • (970) 349-9836 • Lic. #711

Dragonfly Anglers offers guided fly fishing trips for the beginner to the experienced fisherman in Gunnison County and Western Colorado. We fish large rivers, small streams, private water and everything in between.

Also available are guided overnight or day trips to the gold medal Black Canyon of the Gunnison River. Custom overnight trips to our remote lodge in northwestern Gunnison County offer an unforgettable fly fishing experience and provides a different river or stream each day.

Dragonfly Anglers is licensed, bonded and insured and operates under special-use permits from USDA Forest Service, Gunnison National Forest and BLM.

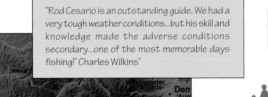

"Rod Cesario is an outstanding guide. We had a very tough weather conditions...but his skill and knowledge made the adverse conditions secondary...one of the most memorable days fishing!" Charles Wilkins"

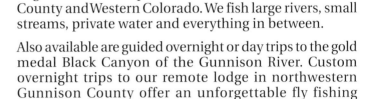

# Eagle Nest Lodge

## Keith Kelly

P.O. Box 509 • Hardin, MT 59034
phone: (406) 665-3711 • fax: (406) 665-3712

Eagle Nest Lodge is one of the world's premier fly-fishing destinations and has the distinction of being one of the first Orvis-endorsed operations. A family business since its conception in 1982, Eagle Nest is owned and managed by the Kellys. The services, lodging and dining of this Montana sporting lodge have satisfied the most discerning anglers for more than a decade.

Eagle Nest is secluded on the banks of the Bighorn River, a fishery heralded as one of the world's finest for the remarkable number of trophy browns and rainbows it holds. Out of the Big Horn Mountains flows the Tongue River, a stream that boasts fantastic scenery in addition to solitude and an abundance of cutthroat, rainbow and brown trout.

"The Bighorn River is a fly-fishing experience every angler should take advantage of...I give Eagle Nest, its staff and guides, my total endorsement" Leigh H. Perkins, Chairman, ORVIS

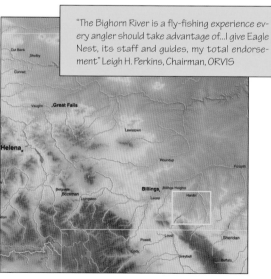

# East Slope Anglers

## Brad Parsch and Wayne Rooney

P.O. Box 160249 • Big Sky, MT 59716
phone: (888) Fly Fysh (359-3974) • (406) 995-4369

Our fishing guides are among the best available. They have the knowledge to be successful and the ability to impart their knowledge in a helpful and friendly manner. From beginner to expert, we can make your fishing experience a rewarding one. Youngsters are welcome.

Float trips are day-long on one of the float-fishing rivers in the area. Wade trips can be arranged for a half or full day with a maximum of three fishermen per guide. Full-day trips include lunch and can involve any number of waters in the area. We also provide instruction by the hour.

One-day and overnight horseback trips to less accessible waters around Big Sky are also available through East Slope Anglers. These trips can be enjoyed with non-fishing members. Most trips involve rides to alpine lakes and the use of float-tubes.

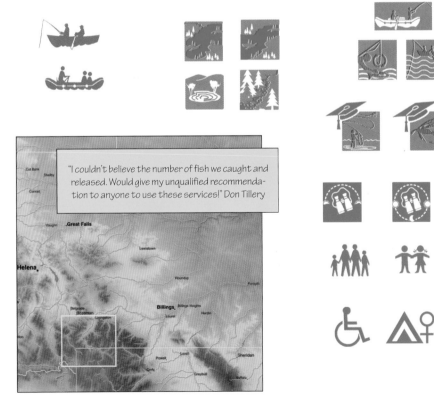

"I couldn't believe the number of fish we caught and released. Would give my unqualified recommendation to anyone to use these services!" Don Tillery

# Esper's Under Wild Skies Lodge & Outfitters

## Vaughn and Judy Esper

P.O. Box 849 • Philipsburg, MT 59858
phone: (406) 859-3000 • fax: (406) 859-3161

Under Wild Skies Lodge and Outfitters is located in the Deerlodge National Forest at the boundary of the Anaconda Pintler Wilderness.

Our guest ranch offers something for everyone. For the fisherman we have two lakes on the ranch. The Middle Fork of Rock Creek, which traverses the property, offers four species of trout. Take a scenic wilderness horseback ride for a day or overnight pack trip into the majestic Pintler mountains, or just relax in the casual elegance of the lodge.

At Under Wild Skies we take pride in our facilities, services and the meticulous attention we pay to every detail of your stay. You come as a guest and leave as a friend.

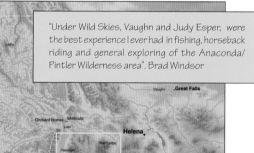

"Under Wild Skies, Vaughn and Judy Esper, were the best experience I ever had in fishing, horseback riding and general exploring of the Anaconda/Pintler Wilderness area". Brad Windsor

# Grossenbacher Guides

## Brian and Jenny Grossenbacher

P.O. Box 6704 • Bozeman, MT 59771
phone: (406) 582-1760 • fax: (406) 582-0589

At Grossenbacher Guides, we guarantee customer service and satisfaction. We not only work hard to get you into fish, but also to fill your expectations of a paramount flyfishing adventure.

Our philosophy, *The Total Flyfishing Experience*, follows the belief that a great day of fishing not only includes plenty of fish, but also an appreciation for the surrounding ecosystems, regional history and geology.

We place a premium on education; whether it's an improvement on your cast, a faster way to tie knots, or a brief lesson in ornithology, you will take home more than just memories of a great trip.

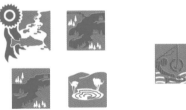

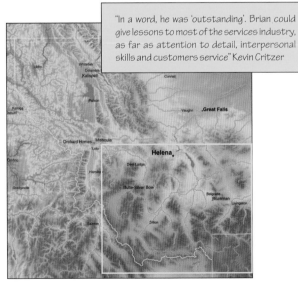

"In a word, he was 'outstanding'. Brian could give lessons to most of the services industry, as far as attention to detail, interpersonal skills and customers service" Kevin Critzer

# Hatch Finders

**Dean A. Reiner**
120 South M St. • Livingston, MT 59047
phone: (406) 222-0989
email: hatchfinders@mcn.net • www. mcn.net/~hatchfinders

Spring and summer fishing on the Yellowstone River can be the challenge of a lifetime. Prolific caddis hatches in May produce the first major dry fly fishing of the year. The river comes alive with aggressive fish beginning with the salmon fly hatch in early July followed by hoppers in August and September.

DePuy's and Armstrong's Spring creeks are the mecca of fly fishing summer or winter. Hatches occur daily along 2.5 miles of the creek. Nymphing and dry fly fishing are not for the faint of heart.

Float trips by drift boats seat two fishermen at a time. Large parties can easily be accommodated. Enjoy the beautiful Paradise Valley where wildlife abounds and the scenery is breathtaking.

"Dean did an outstanding job overall to make my trip a lasting great memory." Capt. Rodney Smith

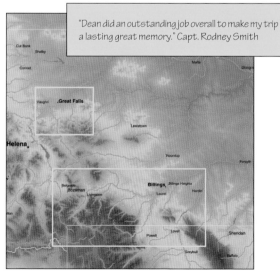

# Heise Expeditions

**Mike Quinn**

5116 E. Heise Rd. • Ririe, ID 83443

phone: (800) 828-3984 • (208) 538-7453 • fax: (208) 538-6039

Heise Resort is nestled in the heart of the world's finest cutthroat trout fishing, just 20 miles east of Idaho Falls. Airport transportation can be arranged; car rentals are available.

Our professional guides are customer-oriented to provide everything necessary for an exciting and enjoyable trip. Experience the beauty, serenity and uniqueness of Idaho's "blueribbon" cutthroat fishing on the South Fork of the Snake River. With hot springs, lodging, golf course and beautiful scenery, you'll get hooked on what we have to offer.

For over 100 years, the family-owned Heise Resort has set traditions of excellence which have kept customers coming back. Blending history with modern recreation, Heise Expeditions continues to provide that unique experience with nature that will keep you coming back.

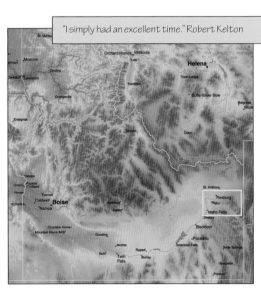

"I simply had an excellent time." Robert Kelton

# John Henry Lee Outfitters, Inc.

## John Lee

Box 8368 • Jackson, WY 83001
phone: (800) 352-2576 • (307) 733-9441 • fax: (307) 733-1403

Come and experience a float-fishing trip with breathtaking views of the Teton Range and the serenity of the wilderness.

We offer guided fishing trips on the Snake, Green and New Fork rivers. In addition, we offer guided walk-in trips to Yellowstone with fishing on the Madison, Firehole, or Yellowstone River.

Backcountry fishing trips vary from seven to ten days in Yellowstone National Park or in the Bridger Teton Wilderness. These areas are considered by many to be the best cutthroat trout fishing in the world. Fish the headwaters of the Yellowstone or Thoroughfare River for an experience you'll always remember.

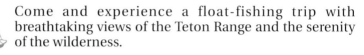

"We can honestly say we enjoyed every minute of each trip and would highly recommend this outfitter to anyone." Jeani Smith

# Love Bros. and Lee, Ltd.

## Ron Fleming and Brenda Nelson

RR#1, Kispiox Rd. • Hazelton, British Columbia, Canada V0J 1Y0
phone/fax: (250) 842-6350

Experience a flyfishing trip of a lifetime in northwestern British Columbia. Our remote wilderness camp is accessible by float plane only.

We offer guided flyfishing for wild rainbow or guided hunting for big game in an exclusive wilderness area, 165 airmiles north of Smithers, British Columbia.

Accommodations are fully-equipped log cabins. A shower is also available.

To ensure you have a personalized quality adventure, we take a maximum of four guests per week.

"Over the 12-13 years with Love Brothers & Lee, my experiences have been great... Brenda and Ron Fleming are the greatest." Sandy Wilkinson

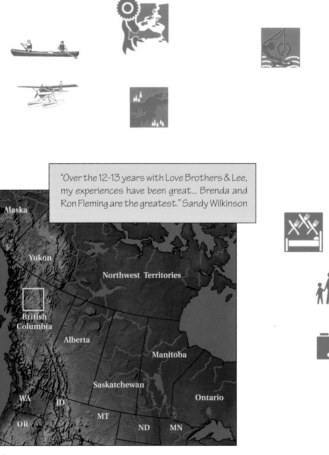

# Mike Wilson's High Mountain Drifters

## Mike Wilson
115 South Wisconsin St. • Gunnison, CO 81230
phone: (800) 793-4243 • (970) 641-4243

High Mountain Drifters is the Gunnison Basin's leading fly shop and guide service. We fish the most diverse and exclusive waters in the area and pride ourselves in making every trip fun. We have male and female guides available, and they are young, experienced and enthusiastic. We offer the highest quality and most miles of private water in the valley. Trips are available for all ages and abilities. Our trips start at 9 a.m. and full day trips get back when you want them to, not at 5 p.m.

We offer free casting clinics every Saturday morning taught by the valley's only two certified casting instructors. We are a full-service, year-round shop and a dealer for Winston, Scott, Redington, Sage, Hexagraph and Cortland rods. We also carry Simms, Fly-Tech, Patagonia and Filson clothing and waders. Our catalog is available upon request.

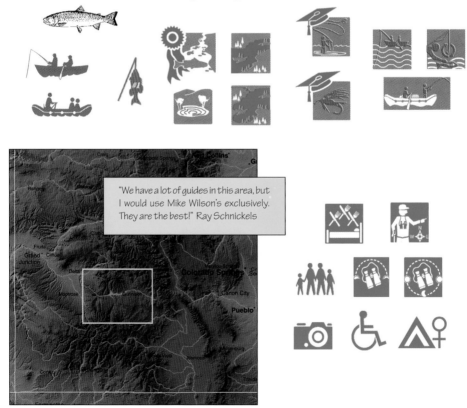

"We have a lot of guides in this area, but I would use Mike Wilson's exclusively. They are the best!" Ray Schnickels

# Rocky Fork Guide Service

## Ernie Strum

HC 50, Box 4849 • Red Lodge, MT 59068
phone: (406) 446-2514

It is our business and great pleasure to offer fly fishing trips tailored to the client's desires. You'll float the Yellowstone, Stillwater or other rivers, fishing from a drift boat and stopping at productive spots to wade and fish from shore. Or, you may prefer a hiking/wading day on a smaller mountain stream, high lake or private pond ... it's up to you.

We'll provide transportation, a hearty shore lunch, tackle and flies if desired, and as much instruction and advice as you wish. Our guides are experienced, licensed and insured.

Outfitter Ernie Strum is a Federation of Fly Fishers-certified casting instructor.

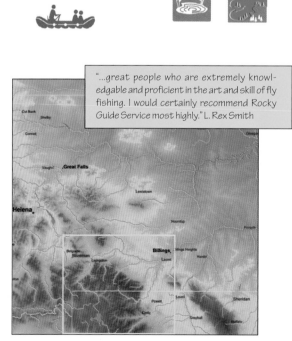

"...great people who are extremely knowledgable and proficient in the art and skill of fly fishing. I would certainly recommend Rocky Guide Service most highly." L. Rex Smith

# Solitude River Trips

**Al and Jeana Bukowsky**

main office: P.O. Box 907 • Merlin, OR 97532
summer (June-August): P.O. Box 702 • Salmon, ID 83467
phone: (800) 396-1776 • www.rivertrips.com

Although just floating the river is an exhilarating and enlightening experience, flyfishermen will find the Middle Fork of the Salmon River a heaven on Earth.

Since 1973, a catch-and-release, single, barbless hook-only policy has been in effect. The native cutthroat trout, the predominant species, has thrived and, along with a few native rainbow and Dolly Varden trout, provides some of the finest fishing in the country. The trout average 12 to 15 inches in length, with some up to 19 inches. You don't even have to be an expert to catch these beautiful fish. Our guides offer patient fly-casting instruction for the novice, while also providing helpful tips for the most experienced angler.

The plentiful trout make the Middle Fork a great place to learn, or to simply improve one's fishing skills.

"Top river float in the West for dry fly action on native Cutthroat...great staff and food." Gene and Debbi Hering

# The Complete Fly Fisher

## David W. and Stuart Decker
Box 127 • Wise River, MT 59762
phone: (406) 832-3175 • fax: (406) 832-3169

There are few places on this earth where legendary water, wild trout and five-star hospitality come together to provide the perfect balance. Where solitude, relaxation, challenge and excitement coexist. This is where life and angling combine to create The Complete Fly Fisher.

What makes one fly fishing experience different from another? Well, there's the river and we've got some of the world's best. There's the level of experience of the angler, or the guide, and we've definitely got the best.

But what really sets your time at The Complete Fly Fisher apart is the hospitality. Our staff and our guides are totally committed to anticipating your needs.

We've fine-tuned the perfect fly fishing experience.

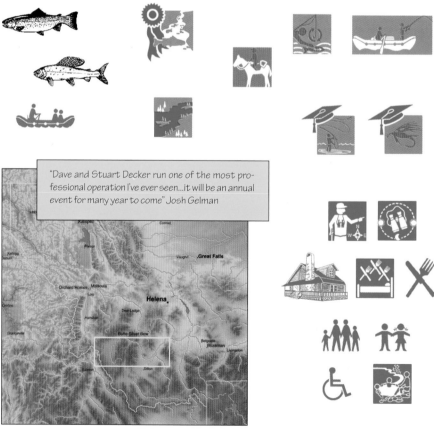

"Dave and Stuart Decker run one of the most professional operation I've ever seen...it will be an annual event for many year to come" Josh Gelman

# The Reel Life

## Manuel J. Monasterio

1100 San Mateo Blvd. NE, Ste. 10 • Albuquerque, NM 87110
510 Montezuma • Santa Fe, NM 87501
phone: (888) 268-3474 • (505) 268-1693

New Mexico is one of fly fishing's best-kept secrets. Excellent weather, beautiful scenery and plentiful trout waters provide truly memorable, year-round fly fishing. Whether you are conducting business in Albuquerque, sight-seeing in Santa Fe or skiing in Taos, our experienced guides can meet you at or drive you to the most productive stretch of water. Choose from world-class, private spring creeks on the Rio Penasco; private stretches on medium-sized tailwaters such as the Cimarron, Costilla or Culebra; and scenic western freestone rivers like the Pecos or Rio Grande; or phenomenal high lakes.

Anglers seeking solitude will enjoy our overnight llama pack trips. Our Albuquerque shop is located 10 minutes from the airport, and our new Santa Fe location is a short walk from the historic plaza district. Both shops offer an extensive selection of Orvis tackle, clothing and gifts.

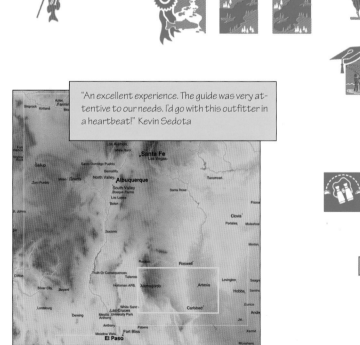

"An excellent experience. The guide was very attentive to our needs. I'd go with this outfitter in a heartbeat!" Kevin Sedota

# The Reflective Angler

**Eric and Al Troth**

P.O. Box 6401 • Bozeman, MT 59771 (winter)
P.O. Box 1307 • Dillon, MT 59725 (summer)
phone: (406) 582-7600 (Bozeman) • (406) 683-2752 (Dillon)

We stalked to within two rod lengths of a large brown trout feeding on mayflies beneath a bank of willows. A perfect cast and the water exploded with a splash as the 20-incher seized the fly. It was the beginning of an unforgettable memory.

I seek to provide the extra dimension and personal attention that makes your trip truly satisfying. I share waters that I know intimately from more than 20 years' experience, and I specialize in instructing the fine points of dry fly and nymphing techniques.

Our daily float/wade excursions to southwestern Montana's blue-ribbon Beaverhead and Big Hole rivers begin in Dillon (a range of accommodations are available). I cater to individuals, pairs and small parties and personally guide all trips.

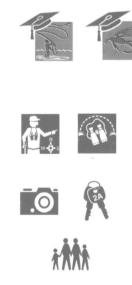

"A first class guide who's main year round profession is guiding fly fishermen. An excellent teacher! He ties and provides all flies for various waters and situation. The BEST!"

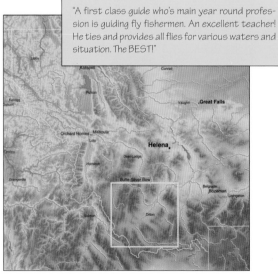

# The Troutfitter

**Dominque Eymere and Bradley Sorock**

313 Elk Ave., PO Box 2779 • Crested Butte, CO 81224
phone: (970) 349-1323 • fax: (970) 349-5066 • Lic. #1655

The Troutfitter is located in the beautiful historic town of Crested Butte, Colorado. We offer walk/wade trips on a variety of exclusive private stretches of water.

We take that extra step to make your trip a pleasurable experience, including a catered lunch from a fine local dining establishment, two-to-one client/guide ratio, and pristine fishing water which we limit to four fisherman per day.

Our guides meet rigorous requirements of experience and are friendly, outgoing and personable.

All trips include any rental needs, including waders, boots, fly vests, and quality flyrods from G-Loomis and St. Croix. Come fish with us.

"Would highly recommended Don for beginner. He is a very patient and a great teacher." Lee Lynch

# Tite Line Fishing

## John Seidel

1520 Pancheri Dr. • Idaho Falls, ID 83402
toll free: (877) LV2-FISH • phone: (208) 529-4343 • fax: (208) 529-4397
email: jseidel@hydeboats.com

Tite Line Fishing offers the absolute best in fly fishing on the Missouri River, and some of the best fishing in all of Montana and the western United States. Our professional resident guides will put you where the fish are. Their enthusiasm helps make them experts on the river's hatches and effective fly patterns. We practice catch and release.

From the beginning angler to the seasoned, Tite Line Fishing will ensure your trip is a lifetime experience. The Missouri River is populated by 5,500 trout per mile with the average length 16 to 17 inches.

In addition to the trout, you will find a variety of Montana wildlife and breathtaking scenery.

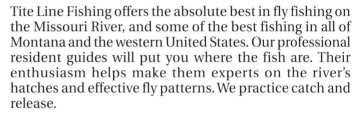

> "One of the very best guided floats I've been on .. very enjoyable, what more could one want!" Robert S. Pulcipher

# Top Rated Freshwater Fishing

## Guides, Outfitters and Lodges

# Careen Lake Lodge

## Jack and Eileen O'Brien

Box 789 • Biggar, Saskatchewan, Canada S0K 0M0
phone: (306) 948-3890

With its many rocky islands, crystal-clear water and beautiful sandy beaches, Careen Lake is without a doubt Saskatchewan's Garden of Eden. This fine lake boasts excellent northern pike, golden walleye, whitefish and lake trout fishing.

The Black Birch River, flowing out of Careen Lake to the northwest, has several enchanting waterfalls that teem with the challenging arctic grayling.

Rates include round-trip air transportation from Buffalo Narrows, boat and motor, and your stay in one of our completely modern units. Light housekeeping units are equipped with propane stove, refrigerator, cooking utensils, etc.

After you've been to Careen, all you have to look forward to is Heaven itself!

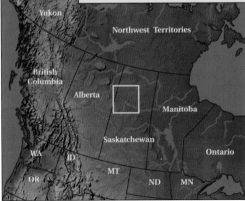

"Jack is an outstanding guide and knows the lake exceptionally well. Can't say enough about O'Brien's Lodge at Careen Lake, Saskatchewan, Canada." Bert Miller

# Flat Iron Outfitting

## Jerry and Brenda Shively

3 Golf Course Rd. • Thompson Falls, MT 59873

phone: (406) 827-3666

Have you ever seen the early morning daylight reflected in the pristine waters of a high mountain lake? Flat Iron Outfitting can provide you with such an experience. Our area has some of the most scenic high lakes in Montana.

It is an added bonus that these lakes also provide excellent trout fishing for the avid angler. We offer day trips into several lakes for both fishing and photography. These are hike-in trips that most people can handle with relative ease.

We also offer late winter to early spring ice fishing trips to these lakes as well as the Clark Fork River. Area rivers also provide some exciting spring and summer stream fishing.

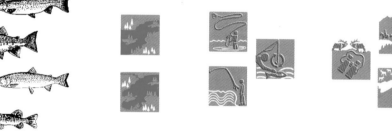

"I would recommend Jerry Shively to anyone who wants a quality experience."

# Granger's Cheemo Lodge

## Clayton Granger

Box 248 • Hardisty, Alberta, Canada T0B 1V0
home phone: (403) 888-2309 (all year)
June 1 - Sept. 30: Saskatchewan Mobile for Uranium City JL3-2959

Cheemo Lodge is situated on Tazin Lake in the northwestern corner of Saskatchewan, Canada. Accessible only by air, we fish two lakes (Tazin and Tsalwar) with approximately 300 square miles of water.

We are a fully modern lodge with hot and cold water to all rooms. Central bathrooms with showers, generated power, freezing facilities and a large rec room with pool table, cards and hot tub. Fishing is very good year-round with the best times being in June and late August to early September.

Give us a try. We're sure we can count on you becoming one of our many regular clients. Good luck and great fishing.

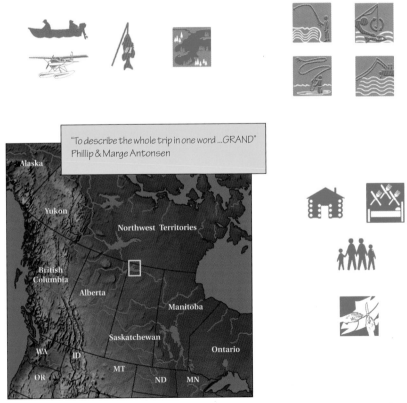

"To describe the whole trip in one word ...GRAND"
Phillip & Marge Antonsen

# Northern Nights Outfitters

### Bruce and Brian Basken

Box 320 • Churchbridge, Saskatchewan, Canada S0A 0M0
phone: (306) 896-2234 • evenings: (306) 896-2271 or (306) 896-2536
email: brian.basken@sk.sympatico.ca

Northern Nights Outfitters, Ltd. offers a great fishing experience. With your group being the only group and our pace being your pace, we ensure that each individual has a holiday to remember.

With a flight over the beautiful northern Saskatchewan landscape, you will fly in to a picturesque, peaceful setting on Waskwei Lake. Your stay will be filled with great fishing for walleye and northern pike

Being family-owned and operated, we will make you feel at home in our clean, comfortable cabin located on a 16-acre island. We are sure that you will enjoy our great home-cooked meals.

For a special family getaway, a quiet and relaxing stay, or a "rip-tear, pull hair" adventure, come and discover Northern Nights.

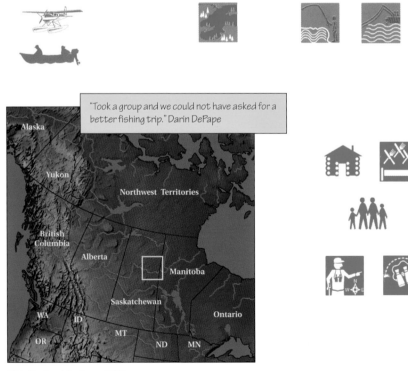

"Took a group and we could not have asked for a better fishing trip." Darin DePape

# Wapiti River Guides

**Gary Lane**

P.O. Box 1125 • Riggins, ID 83549
phone: (800) 488-9872 • (208) 628-3523 • fax: (208) 628-3523
email: wapitirg@cyberhighway.net

Float Idaho's Salmon River by driftboat for Chukar hunting and Steelhead fishing combination trips. Flowing through the second deepest gorge in North America, the river will introduce you to steep, rugged terrain.

After traversing the breathtaking terra firma with your dog (if you like), come back to the boats and relax with a fishing rod in your hands — that is, until a magnificent red-sided Steelhead takes your line into the sky.

We place two clients per driftboat and send a baggage boat and crew ahead to secure camps, which allows us more time to hunt and fish between destinations.

Trips range from one to six days. Chukar/Steelhead trips are offered only on the Salmon River. Steelhead fishing is offered on both the Salmon and Oregon's Grande Ronde River, a fly fishermen's paradise. Whitewater and scenic trips are also offered.

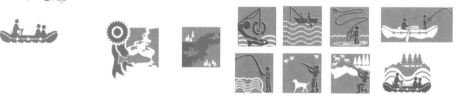

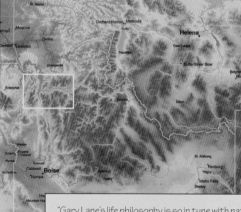

"Gary Lane's life philosophy is so in tune with nature and his environment that one is totally immersed in the experience and emerges refreshed." Roy and Kristi Wilson

# Western Waters and Woods

**Jerry Nichols**

5455 Keil Loop • Missoula, MT 59802

phone: (800) 757-1680 PIN #2060 • (406) 543-3203

email: waters@bigsky.net • www.bigsky.net/westernwaters

Western Waters and Woods, established in 1976, is a family-owned and operated whitewater, fishing, charter boat and hunting guide service based in Missoula, Montana.

As a Montana native, I take great pride in being a licensed outfitter in the state of Montana, and offer daily or extended trips in both Montana and Alaska. We are the original outfitter of whitewater float trips through the now famous Alberton Gorge on the Clark Fork River. We float the whitewater and blue ribbon trout streams of Montana. The Clark Fork, Madison, Big Hole and Missouri rivers offer breathtaking whitewater and trophy trout fishing.

"Jerry's knowledge and skills level are only found in someone who has spent their lives on or around rivers...one of the best!"

# Top Rated

# Outdoor Wilderness Adventures

## Guides and Outfitters

# WSRT/"Birds of Prey" Expeditions

## Steve Guinn

4519 N. MountainView Drive • Boise, ID 83704
phone: 208-327-8903 • fax: 208-376-5858

Owner, Outfitter and Operator ofWhitewater Shop River Tours/"Birds of Prey" Expeditions has organized and led tours into the Snake River "Birds of Prey" National Conservation Area for over 19 years.

WSRT/Birds of Prey Expeditions has created these tours with your comfort in mind. Our boats are large and well equipped with PA systems so everyone can hear the information. On all trips with food, we are sure you will be delighted with our menu.

The Snake River "Birds of Prey" National Conservation Area is located in a spectacular canyon. Our guides focus on the Natural History, Geology & Bird watching. The guides are very informative and have been studying and working the area for many years. Bring along your binoculars, cameras and a tape recorder if you choose.

Each year Steve guides as many as 1000 Idaho school children in his "classrooms in the wild" school tours (subsidized).

> Our entire 5th grade at Liberty School have enjoyed a fun exciting and informative day on the river with Steve and his son for the last 3 years. We look forward to returning year after year!" Linda Thoreson, Liberty School

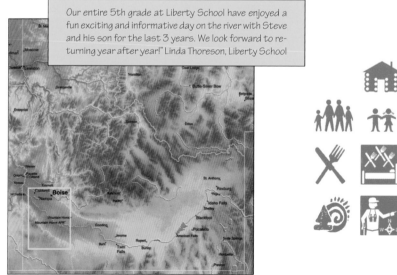

# WSRT/"Birds of Prey" Expeditions

# Top Rated River Adventures

## Guides and Outfitters

# Bill Dvořak's Kayak & Rafting Expeditions

## Bill and Jaci Dvořak

17921 U.S. Hwy. 285 • Nathrop, CO 81236
reservations: (800) 824-3795 • office: (719) 539-6851 • fax: (719) 539-3378
email: dvorakex@rmii.com • http://www.vtinet.com/dvorak

Bill and I invite you to join us for the adventure of a lifetime. We have been guiding river and wilderness trips since 1969 and have one of the most experienced and best trained staffs in the industry. We have successfully combined high adventure with professionalism for more than 25 years. We've watched our children grow up on the river, we've seen the staff and guests respond to being on the river, and we know there is a powerful moving effect a river has on us all.

Everyone deserves a chance to experience such river magic. Our trips make it easy for you to enjoy the best of whitewater beauty and adventure. Choose the trip that best suits you, or ask for a customized group trip.

Make this season your year for the adventure of a lifetime!

"Everything they do is first class and when you leave, you feel like you are leaving family."
Walter L. Fuller

**Ed DVOŘÁK'S**
KAYAK & RAFTING
EXPEDITIONS

# Canoe North Adventures

## Al Pace and Lin Ward

RR#1, Orangeville • Ontario, Canada L9W 2Y8
phone: (519) 941-6654 • fax: (519) 941-4503

Canoe North offers spectacular wilderness canoe expeditions in Canada's Yukon and Northwest Territories. Guides Al Pace and Lin Ward take pride in building compatible groups of ten trippers with matching skill levels to ensure solid group dynamics. No-trace camping skills and whitewater paddling strokes are taught to ensure maximum safety and a genuine respect for the remote wilderness regions travelled. Each trip provides personal time for wildlife photography, writing , hiking, and world-class fly fishing. Wildlife viewing includes moose, caribou, musk-ox, grizzly and black bear, wolves, fox, sheep, eagles, falcons, cranes and geese. Our top-quality camping gear and hearty gourmet camp meals combined with twenty years of guiding experience ensure that your wilderness adventure will be unforgettable!

Canoe North river trips are rated novice, intermediate or expert and run ten - fourteen days in length. They include The Wind, Bonnet Plume, Firth and Snake Rivers of the Northern Yukon and the Kazan, Thelon, Coppermine and Burnside of the Northwest Territories.

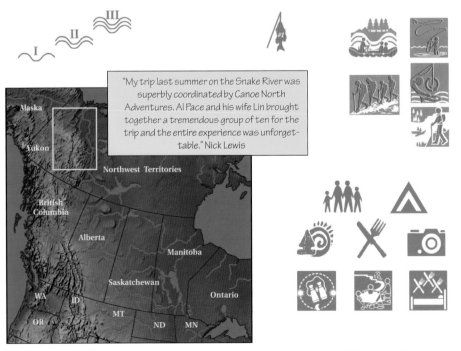

"My trip last summer on the Snake River was superbly coordinated by Canoe North Adventures. Al Pace and his wife Lin brought together a tremendous group of ten for the trip and the entire experience was unforgettable." Nick Lewis

# Headwaters River Company

**Conrad Fourney and Betsy Bader**

P. O. Box 1 • Banks, ID 83602

phone: (800) 800 RAFT (7238) • (208) 793-2348

email: rafting@micron.net • http://netnow.micron.net/~rafting/

The Payette rivers are the whitewater state's best-kept secret. With Headwaters you can explore the South Fork, North Fork or Main Payette. The Payette River system contains a myriad of opportunities for whitewater experiences, from a scenic Class I float to an adrenaline pumping, white-knuckled Class IV ride. Choose from half-day, one-day, or multi-day trips.

It is our goal to provide each of our guests with the best river trip, from the guide and food to the whitewater. We have wonderful kayak instructors who have a penchant for teaching. The only prerequisite is an attitude for fun. Our guides average eight years guiding experience and are licensed by the state of Idaho. All full-time guides hold First Responder medical cards.

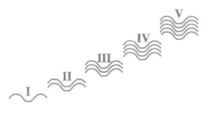

"An outstanding whitewater experience by a friendly, professional staff...A remarkable trip" Tom Lillie

HEADWATERS
RIVER COMPANY

# Idaho Afloat

## Bruce Howard

P.O. Box 542 • Grangeville, ID 83530
phone: (800) 700-2414 • (208) 983-2414 • fax: (208) 983-9259
email: idafloat@camesnet.com • www.idafloat.com

Idaho Afloat provides deluxe whitewater rafting adventures on the Snake River through Hells Canyon and on the Lower Salmon River. Our trips offer families, first-time and experienced rafters a variety of multi-day soft adventure excitement.

The Snake River through Hells Canyon (rated Class IV) is the deepest canyon in North American and has the most powerful whitewater in the Northwest. You will run the rapids, see ancient pictographs, explore old homesteads, hike riverside trails, and have time to relax and enjoy the sounds of nature.

The Lower Salmon River Gorge (Class III) offers solitude, four spectacular canyons, and incredible white sandy beaches with clear and cool pools for swimming and daydreaming.

Join Idaho Afloat for a memory of a lifetime. Sit back and let it happen.

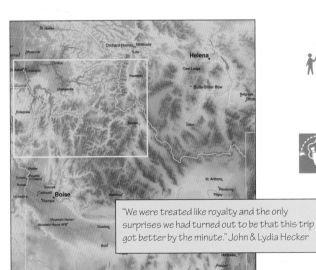

"We were treated like royalty and the only surprises we had turned out to be that this trip got better by the minute." John & Lydia Hecker

# Mild to Wild Rafting

**Alex and Molly Mickel**

11 Rio Vista Circle • Durango, CO 81302
phone: (800) 567-6745 • (970) 247-4789 • fax: (970) 382-0545
email: mildwild@rmii.com • http://www.mild2wildrafting.com

Mild to Wild Rafting has a river trip for all ages (3-93) and all adventure levels in beautiful Southwest Colorado.

Enjoy a family trip (two hours to four days) on the Animas, San Juan, or Dolores rivers. Experience an intermediate trip on the Upper Dolores or Upper Piedra rivers (nine full days). For high adventure try the big drops of the Piedra River (one to two days), or go for an adrenaline rush on one of the toughest commercially-run rivers in the USA — the Upper Animas River (one to three days).

We guarantee your absolute delight with our services and guides or the trip is on us. Call for a free color brochure.

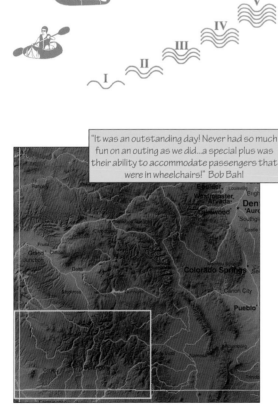

"It was an outstanding day! Never had so much fun on an outing as we did...a special plus was their ability to accommodate passengers that were in wheelchairs!" Bob Bahl

# Nahanni Wilderness Adventures

## David and Wendy Hibbard

Box 4, Site 6 R.R.1 • Didsbury, Alberta, Canada T0M 0W0
phone: (888) 897-5223 • phone/fax: (403) 637-3843
email: adventures@nahanniwild.com • www.nahanniwild.com

Flowing from the heart of the MacKenzie Mountains in Canada's Northwest Territories, the South Nahanni River is steeped in legend and unsurpassed in natural beauty. Its reputation as a pristine and spectacular wilderness river has earned it recognition the world over. Affectionately called Canada's River of Gold, the Nahanni offers its travelers an abundance of natural treasurer. The fresh alpine meadows and soaring peaks of the upper river, the thundering cataract of Virginia Falls, the awesome canyons and abundant wildlife make the Nahanni region a kaleidoscope of natural beauty, virtually untouched by people.

Legendary prospectors were lured to the Nahanni seeking their fortune in gold, but it eluded them.

We guarantee you will return home with a wealth of photographs and unforgettable memories.

"A rare and memorable experience for my 50th birthday" Doug Christie

**Nahanni**
*Wilderness Adventures*

# Northwest Voyageurs

**Jeff Peavey**

P.O. Box 373 • Lucile, ID 83542

reservations: (800) 727-9977 • phone: (208) 628-3021 • fax: (208) 628-3780

email: nwvoyage@voyageurs.com • http://voyageurs.com

We take pleasure in turning what you think will be an interesting trip into a once-in-a lifetime experience. We never tire of being told, "There simply aren't words to describe it! Our senses come alive! The thrill was unimaginable."

We're owner-operated, focusing on intimate, quality trips to the best places we know and love. You will quickly understand why more than 70% of the 6,000 plus friends who joined us last year were returning clients or referrals. I personally guarantee you 100% satisfaction!

We use new self-bailing rafts and kayaks, Coast Guard-inspected and -approved life jackets, and waterproof containers for your clothes and cameras. We provide a four-person tent for every two people, plus camp tables and lawn chairs, cocktail ice, refreshing drinks and hors d'oeuvres. After the guides work their culinary magic all waste is packed up and carried out for recycling.

"I never questioned that they'd keep us all safe, entertained, well-fed, and laughing throughout the entire trip." Kristine Schmalz

**Northwest Voyageurs**

# Rocky Mountain River Tours

## Dave and Sheila Mills

P.O. Box 2552 • Boise, ID 83701
phone: (208) 345-2400 • fax: (208) 756-4808
summer: P.O. Box 207 • Salmon, ID 83467 • phone: (208) 756-4808

The primitive, awesome Middle Fork of the Salmon, one of the original eight rivers to be designated Wild and Scenic by Congress in 1980, is still untamed and, for the most part, untouched. Like the Main Salmon, it meanders through the Frank Church River of No Return Wilderness Area. Its whitewater is rated up to Class V in May and June; Class IV in July and August. It's an extraordinary stream, and the outfitters that run it are all top-notch. Even in that company, the six-day, 105 mile trip run by Rocky Mountain River Tours (founded in 1978) stands out.

Owners Dave and Sheila Mills use two paddleboats (accommodating six), four oar boats (accommodating four), and four inflatable single-passenger kayaks. There's one guide for every four guests.

Sheila Mills's Dutch-oven cooking is an essential part of the experience. Exceptional food belongs in this exceptional environment.

"This company was our 3rd on the Middle Fork & definitely the best!" McSwain Family

# Sheri Griffith Expeditions, Inc.

## Sheri Griffith

P.O. Box 1324 • 2231 South Highway 191 • Moab, UT 84532
phone: (800) 332-2439 • (435) 259-8229 • fax: (435) 259-2226
email: classriver@aol.com • www.GriffithExp.com

Enjoy the excitement of the outdoors without the work. Utah river rafting journeys, two- to six-day trips on the Colorado, Green and Dolores rivers through national parks and wild and scenic stretches. We make you comfortable in the wilderness and take care of all the details. No experience necessary. Professional guides, state-of-the-art equipment and excellent safety record combine to create an unforgettable experience. Choose from the larger stable rafts to the smaller high-action boats.

This is our 27th year rafting the best rivers of the Southwest. Some specialties include, "Family Goes to Camp," "Women Only," and "Luxury Expeditions," or, let us design a custom trip for you. Free 24-page brochure and video available.

"My father and I agree this was one of our best trips ever. The guides and the people were wonderful, the food was amazing, and the trip overall was incredible!" Maria Marsh and Dad, Joel

Sheri Griffith Expeditions, Inc.

# Solitude River Trips

## Al and Jeana Bukowsky

main office: P.O. Box 907 • Merlin, OR 97532
summer (June, July, August): PO Box 702, Salmon, ID 83467
phone: (800) 396-1776 • (541) 479-1876 • fax: (541) 471-2235
www.rivertrips.com

Idaho's Middle Fork of the Salmon River is spectacular beyond imagination. It carves and churns through 105 miles of the most rugged, inaccessible and primitive country in the United States — a country still relatively untouched by man. There are no roads. It's wild and untamed.

Our guides are licensed professionals with years of boating and fly fishing experience. Solitude River Trips is a bonded, licensed outfitter and guide service.

Without roads, and with limited trail access due to the canyon's rugged nature, the Middle Fork is best seen, explored and fished by floating the river. It is truly a wondrous journey.

Come join us and share the spirit of adventure.

"If there was a rating higher than outstanding, I would have marked that instead. Al & Jeana run a 5-star outfit!" Shelly Smith

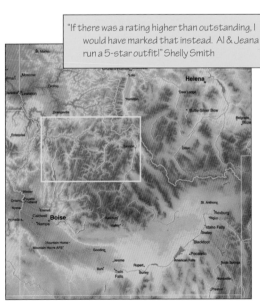

# Wapiti River Guides

## Gary Lane

P.O. Box 1125 • Riggins, ID 83549
phone: (800) 488-9872 • (208) 628-3523 • fax: (208) 628-3523
email: wapitirg@cyberhighway.net

Wapiti River Guides owner Gary Lane is a modern-day mountain/river man — a tipi dweller living close to nature — who offers new meaning to offbeat trips.

If you enjoy wilderness folklore, natural history, close nature encounters and a unique experience led by a trained wildlife biologist, then this trip is for you and your family.

Trips are conducted with a combination of whitewater dory, raft, and inflatable kayaks. Rapids range from Class III-V on Idaho's Lower Salmon and Oregon's Grand Ronde and Owyhee rivers.

Each journey is strictly limited to small groups. If you wish for solitude, personalized experiences and time away from mass transit affairs, come with Wapiti. Why flock with magpies when you can soar with eagles?

Trips from half to several days' duration offer chukar hunting and steelhead and fly fishing. Specialized workshops include primitive survival skills, yoga and outdoor education.

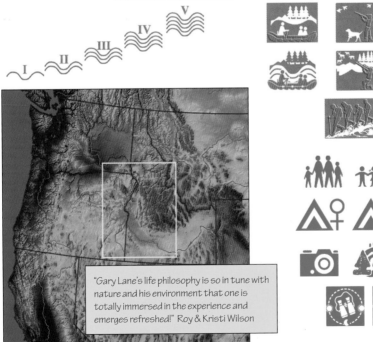

"Gary Lane's life philosophy is so in tune with nature and his environment that one is totally immersed in the experience and emerges refreshed!" Roy & Kristi Wilson

WAPITI

# Warren River Expeditions, Inc.

**David Warren**

P.O. Box 1375 • Salmon, ID 83467

phone: (800) 765-0421 • (208) 756-6387 • (208) 756-4495 • fax: (208) 756-3910

email: salmonriver@raftidaho.com • http://www.raftidaho.com

If you have ever wanted to take a whitewater rafting trip but didn't want to camp out, Warren River Expeditions, Inc. has the perfect trip for you.

Spend six days in Idaho's Frank Church River of No Return Wilderness and on the Main Salmon River. You will run exciting whitewater and spend each night in a different backcountry lodge. It is a very unique trip and one you will remember always.

While on the river we have the excitement of a whitewater river trip with fishing, hiking, horseback riding and all the adventure of a wilderness trip, with a few amenities of home.

"The food was above & beyond what anyone would expect, and all the equipment was in perfect condition. I would recommend this outfitter to everyone...I have already booked my next trip!" Connie Eliott

# Warren River Expeditions

# Western Waters and Woods

**Jerry Nichols**

5455 Keil Loop • Missoula, MT 59802

phone: (800) 757-1680 PIN #2060 • (406) 543-3203

email: waters@bigsky.net • http://www.bigsky.net/westernwaters

Western Waters and Woods is a family-owned guide and outfitter service established in 1976 by Montana native Gerald R. Nichols. We operate as a whitewater, fishing, charter boat, and hunting guide service based in Missoula, Montana. I take great pride in being a state-licensed outfitter, and offer day or extended trips in Montana and Alaska.

We float the whitewater and fish the blue ribbon trout streams of Montana. We are the original outfitter of whitewater float trips through the now-famous Alberton Gorge on the Clark Fork River. The Clark Fork, Madison, Big Hole and Missouri rivers offer breathtaking white water and trophy trout fishing.

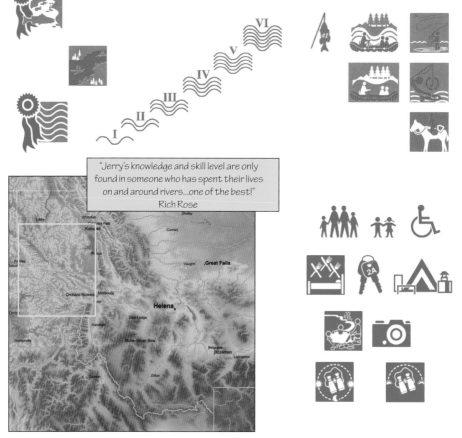

"Jerry's knowledge and skill level are only found in someone who has spent their lives on and around rivers...one of the best!"
Rich Rose

# Whitewater Voyageurs

**John Sells**

P.O. Box 346 • Poncha Springs, CO 81242
phone: (800) 255-2585 • (719) 539-7618 • fax: (719) 539-7610
email: john@mtnspts.com • www.mtnspts.com

Whitewater Voyageurs has successfully operated on the Arkansas River for more than 20 years. We are proud to offer the most highly-trained and experienced staff in the industry.

We respect our guests' needs and do everything within reason to ensure their satisfaction. With our motivated and knowledgeable team, we maintain our commitment to excellence and continually offer higher quality, more innovative adventure packages. In a world of constant environmental abuse, we vow to take every action possible to uphold the pristine majesty of the Rocky Mountain area we inhabit.

Whitewater Voyageurs is a member of the Colorado River Outfitters Association, Arkansas River Outfitters Association, America Outdoors, and licensed through the state of Colorado as a commercial river outfitter.

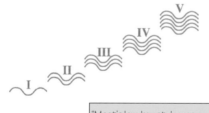

"Moot's low-key style was a perfect balance for an exciting and sometimes heartstopping experience...what a blast!" Lisa Stockton

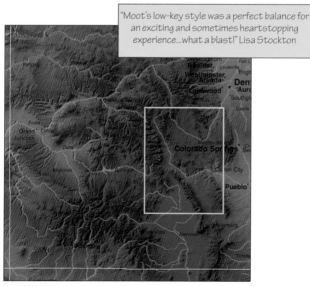

# WHITEWATER VOYAGEURS

# Wild Rockies Tours

## Gail Gutsche, Matt Thomas, Dan Ward

P.O. Box 8184 • Missoula, MT 59807
phone: (406) 728-0566 • fax: (406) 728-4134
email: gutsche@wildrockies.org

Wild Rockies Tours specializes in three- to eight-day canoe trips on the Missouri, Yellowstone, Clark Fork and Blackfoot rivers, located in beautiful Montana. Opportunities for wildlife viewing are frequent and often thrilling. Birding is spectacular; sightings of bald and golden eagles are common . Our small group tours — minimum of four, maximum of eight — assures that our guests receive plenty of personal attention and allows us to travel lightly on the land. Tasty camp meals, first-rate equipment and trained guides provided. Custom tours and mountaineering trips available on request.

Celebrate Lewis and Clark's famous expedition. This eight-day canoe tour of the Wild and Scenic Missouri River features mild paddling through the remote Missouri Breaks and White Cliffs, which has changed little since the time of the famous captains.

NOTE: We do not fish or raft.

"It was an adventure of a lifetime! Our comfort and security were top priorities at all times!" Robert Ward

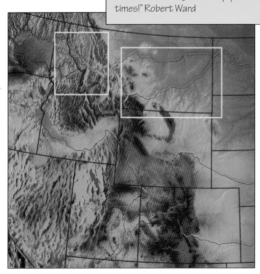

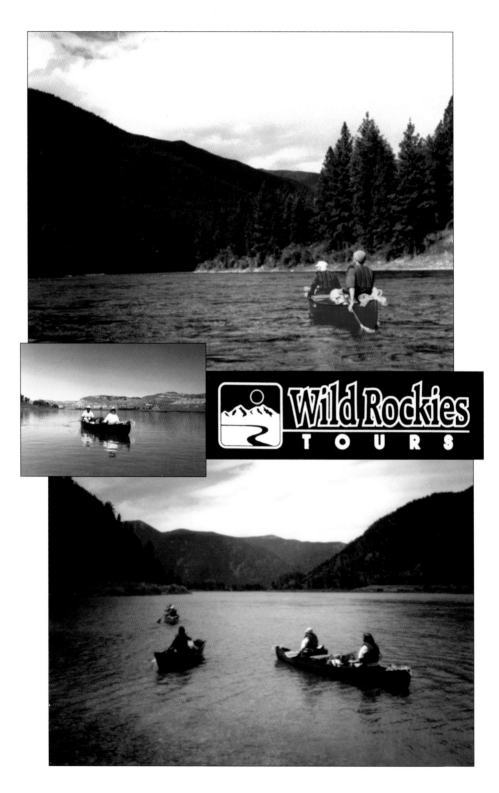

# Top Rated Western Adventures

## Ranches, Pack Stations & Outfitters

# Beaver Meadows Resort Ranch

## Don and Linda Weixelman

100 Marmot Dr. #1 • Po Box 178 • Red Feather Lakes, CO 80545
phone: (800) 462-5870 • (970) 881-2450 • fax: (970) 881-2643
email: bmrr@verinet.com

Beaver Meadows is a full-service destination resort with a relaxed, family-oriented atmosphere in a breathtaking setting. Located on the North Fork of the Cache La Poudre River, our ranch occupies 320 acres of mountain meadows, willow creeks, lodgepole forests and quaking aspen groves.

Open year-round, we've provided group and vacation services for more than 20 years. Our staff is committed to providing individual attention and quality service to every event that we host.

We offer year-round activities. Our 22-mile trail system is used for extensive equine activities, mountain biking, hiking, cross-country skiing and showshoeing. Lessons and guides are available for all these activities. Activities are not included in our nightly rates unless a package is requested.

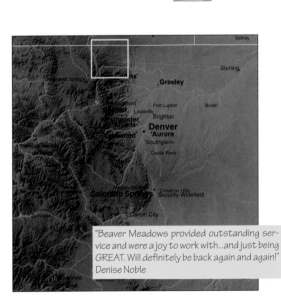

"Beaver Meadows provided outstanding service and were a joy to work with...and just being GREAT. Will definitely be back again and again!"
Denise Noble

# Beaver Meadows Resort Ranch

# Boulder Lake Lodge

**Kim Bright**

Box 1100H • Pinedale, WY 82941

phone: (800) 788-5401 • (307) 537-5400

Boulder Lake Lodge, located on the west slope of the remote and rugged Wind River Mountain Range, serves as headquarters for our many varied pack trip operations.

We offer guided trips ranging from hourly rides out of our rustic lodge to ten-day excursions high into the Bridger Wilderness Area. There are no roads!

Trails wind through some of the most spectacular high mountain scenery in this country at around 10,000 feet elevation. We pride ourselves in our fine horses and mules. We have a clean, professionally-staffed lodge and camp.

Exclusive groups with four or more.

"The pleasant family atmosphere and delicious meals at this secluded ranch were delightful and the professional handling of our spot pack into the surrounding mountain was excellent!" Cynthia Fisher

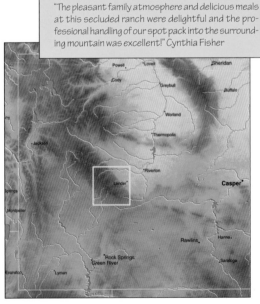

# Broken Arrow Lodge

## Erwin and Sherry Clark

2200 Upper Ruby Rd., Box 177 • Alder, MT 59710
phone: (800) 775-2928 • phone/fax: (406) 842-5437
www.recworld.com/state/mt/hunt/broken/broken.html

Broken Arrow Lodge is located in the Snowcrest Mountain Range in Southwest Montana's Ruby Valley. The Ruby River flows through the property and is only a moment's walk away.

Broken Arrow Lodge is a modern facility known for friendly, personalized service in a homey atmosphere. We supply lodging, meals (served at your convenience), and year-round recreation. Activities include fishing, hunting, family vacations, horseback riding, wildlife viewing, winter sports, lodge activities, and more.

Five rooms are available with space for one to four, or a family-size room with space for up to eight. Rooms are clean and comfortable with your choice of single or double beds. Large front deck provides a great area to relax and view the breathtaking scenery, abundant wildlife, and beautiful wildflowers.

Airport shuttle service is available as well as equipment rental, fax, and satellite TV.

> "The hospitality was wonderful...we felt like we were visiting friends" Mary Ann McGuire

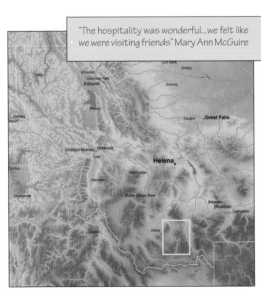

# Cheff Guest Ranch

## Mick and Karen Cheff
4274 Eagle Pass Rd. • Charlo, MT 59824
phone: (406) 644-2557

A world of wondrous natural beauty and superb outdoor recreation awaits you at the Cheff Guest Ranch.

The working cattle and horse ranch lies on a mountainside overlooking the beautiful Mission Valley. Explore the beauty of our area on foot or horseback.

Flathead Lake, the National Bison Range, and Glacier National Park are just a few of the scenic and historic attractions located nearby. Fishing and scenic pack trips in the Bob Marshall and Mission Mountain Wilderness begin in early July. They are a once-in-a-lifetime experience, yet many take the trips repeatedly.

We are one of Montana's oldest outfitting families with more than 65 years of experience. Our experience and desire to please you combine for a memorable, and we hope, successful trip.

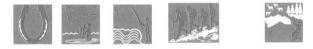

"Their service is outstanding and they always go the extra mile to help in any way", Carol Fisher

CHEFF GUEST
RANCH
Outfitters and Guides

# Darby Mountain Outfitters

## R. John Harper and Chuck Thornton

P.O. Box 447 • Big Piney, WY 83113

phone: R.John Harper (307) 276-3934 • Chuck Thornton (307) 386-9220

Pack trips are our specialty. From late June through September catch the fragrances of spring, see newborn wildlife, and enjoy colorful Indian autumns.

Our pack trips travel through an isolated mountain range in the center of the Wyoming Rockies, a place few people have seen.

Enjoy majestic scenery, fish mountain lakes for cutthroat and brook trout, and eat healthy western campfire meals under our big sky.

Experienced guides/packers will fit you to a horse and teach you how to ride in the mountains.

Just bring an adventuresome spirit and we will provide the rest!

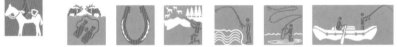

"This experience is not for the faint of heart. Chuck Thornton offers a variety of mountain trips that caters to both the novice, as well as the most experienced horseman" Richard M. Saroney

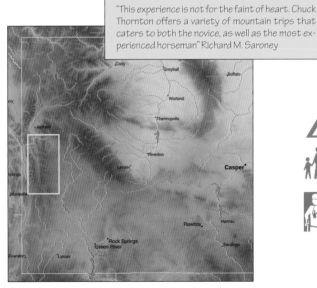

# Darby Mountain Outfitters

Big Piney, Wyoming

# Darwin Ranch

**Loring Woodman**

P.O. Box 511 • Jackson, WY 83001
phone: (307) 733-5588 • fax: (307) 739-0885

The Darwin Ranch has been catering to wilderness enthusiasts since 1965 when Loring Woodman began renovating the old log cabins which lay along the original, now obliterated, pioneer wagon track into Jackson Hole.

We are 22 miles inside Teton National Forest and have the last totally-isolated section of the Gros Ventre River to ourselves. Modern plumbing, electricity from Kinky Creek, a library, piano, and an accomplished, imaginative cook, complete the scene. Our maximum of 20 guests have a minimally-organized existence doing exactly what they want: riding, hiking, climbing, packtripping, and fly fishing.

The entire ranch, located 30 miles of Jackson Hole, is available in winter for private gatherings of six to 12.

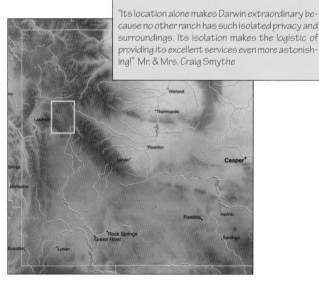

"Its location alone makes Darwin extraordinary because no other ranch has such isolated privacy and surroundings. Its isolation makes the logistic of providing its excellent services even more astonishing!" Mr. & Mrs. Craig Smythe

# Double Spear Ranch

## Tony and Donna Blackmore
P.O. Box 43 • Pryor, MT 59066
phone: (406) 259-8291 • fax: (406) 245-7673
email: DoubleSpearRanch@juno.com

We invite adventurous city slickers to join us and live the real West for a week or two on our working cattle ranch 35 miles south of Billings, Montana, on the Crow Indian Reservation. Although a relative of old Sitting Bull, your cowboss Tony Blackmore will remind you more of John Wayne. Ride the range and the mountains, work cattle, learn colt-breaking and horsemanship techniques, and enjoy cowboy cookouts. You will ride quarter horses and meet rare (hypoallergenic!) American curly horses — buffalo — and lots more livestock and pets. This isn't a fancy upscale vacation; you will join in and experience real ranch life. Expect a little dust, a little sweat, and tons of laughter.

We include your own horse, unlimited riding, ranch meals cowboy-style, airport pickup and delivery. Bedrooms for adults in ranch house or bunkhouse (shared facilities).

Special 2-week western youth camps for guests 13-19.

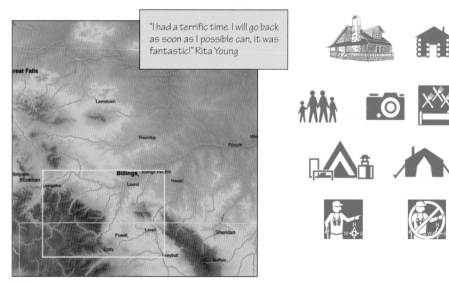

"I had a terrific time. I will go back as soon as I possible can, it was fantastic!" Rita Young

# Early Guest Ranch

## Ruth and Wayne Campbell

7374 US Hwy. 26 • Crowheart, WY 82512 (summer)
1624 Hwy. S • Wentzville, MO 63385 (winter)
phone: (307) 455-4055 (summer) (314) 332-1234 (winter) • fax: (314) 639-5250
email: earlyranch@aol.com • www.earlyranch.com

Welcome, pardner. This is where you live the cowboy way. For one unforgettable week, the spirit of the West will invade your world. Leave your phones and stress behind and escape to a world of breathtaking skies and awe-inspiring Rocky Mountain scenery.

Horseback ride to your heart's content or just kick back and relax. Daily riding instructions leads the list of exciting ranch activities, which include self-guided river trips by canoe or raft, fly or rod fishing on the gorgeous Wind River, hiking, photography, knot-tying classes, square dancing and horseshoes, evening sing-along campfires, and stargazing. Kids love our "up and at 'em" Lil' Buckaroo program.

Our unique Sunrise Spa features aerobic classes, tanning, exercise machines and hot tub. The day's itinerary is tacked to your cabin door … do as much or as little as you care to. Boy-howdy, ya tired yet?

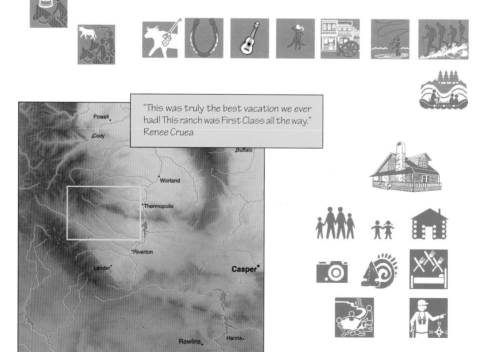

"This was truly the best vacation we ever had! This ranch was First Class all the way."
Renee Cruea

# EARLY
## Guest Ranch

# Echo Canyon Guest Ranch

## David Hampton

P.O. Box 328 • LaVeta, CO 81055
phone: (800) 341-6603 • (719) 742-5524 • fax: (719) 742-5525
email: echo@rmi.net • www.guestecho.com • Lic. #1143

Echo Canyon affords its guests a "unique western adventure." We're proud of our quality riding program for beginners as well as riders who can work cattle. We match our riders with athletic horses that we own and train.

Your "unique western adventure" includes trail rides, roping lessons, cattle work, overnight pack trip, cookout, cowboy entertainment, trout ponds, shooting range, 4 x 4 tours, game area, hot tub, delicious food, quality rooms and cabins.

Our scenery is spectacular. We are located at 8,500 feet elevation beneath West Spanish Peak in Southern Colorado where wildlife abounds.

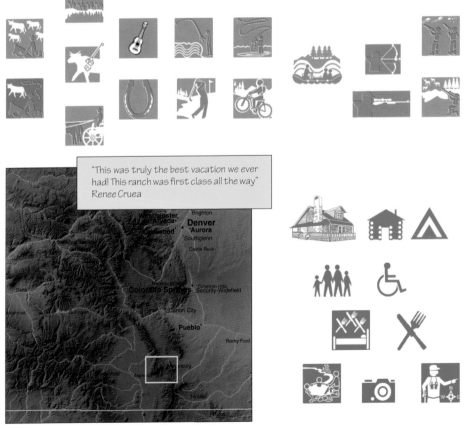

"This was truly the best vacation we ever had! This ranch was first class all the way"
Renee Cruea

# Esper's Under Wild Skies Lodge & Outfitters

### Vaughn and Judy Esper

P.O. Box 849 • Philipsburg, MT 59858

phone: (406) 859-3000 • fax: (406) 859-3161

Under Wild Skies Lodge and Outfitters is located in the Deerlodge National Forest at the boundary of the Anaconda Pintler Wilderness.

Our guest ranch offers something for everyone. For the fisherman we have two lakes on the ranch. The Middle Fork of Rock Creek traverses through the property and offers four species of trout. Take a scenic wilderness horseback ride for a day or an overnight pack trip into the majestic Pintler Mountains. Or, just relax in the casual elegance of the lodge.

At Under Wild Skies we take pride in our facilities, services, and the meticulous attention we pay to every detail of your stay. You come as a guest and leave as a friend.

"Wonderful experience, beautiful location, beautiful location, great cooking, 'unmatched'!" Mr. & Mrs. Ronald Vachon

# EW Watson & Sons Outfitting

## Ed and Wanda Watson

7837 U.S. Hwy. 287 • Townsend, MT 59644
phone: (800) 654-2845 • fax: (406) 266-4498

### Where the only thing better than the scenery is the Service

E W Watson & Sons Outfitting is dedicated to providing top hands, quality horses, and an educational and affordable vacation.

Customize your trip to your pleasure. Explore these opportunities: horseback pack-in camping trips; mountain lake fly fishing trips; covered wagon trips; Missouri River float trips; and, authentic working ranch cattle drives.

Combine local historical points of interest with ranch home lodging. Visit Elkhorn Ghost Town, tour Lewis and Clark Caverns, ride the tour train at Helena and learn about the colorful gold rush days.

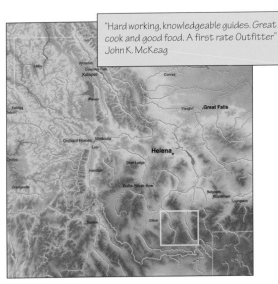

"Hard working, knowledgeable guides. Great cook and good food. A first rate Outfitter"
John K. McKeag

# Frazier Outfitting

## Sammy Frazier

HC 34, Box 81 • Rye, CO 81069
phone: (719) 676-2964 • license #1738

We are a horseback operation offering full service tent camps at an elevation of 11,300 feet. This includes the option of taking day rides from the base camps to 13,000 feet. The alpine terrain provides spectacular opportunities for photography, nature study, wildlife viewing, fishing and relaxing. Of particular interest are the small lakes and miles of high-country streams filled with trout, along with abundant herds of wild elk grazing the meadows and drainages.

We also offer pack-in/out service for campers and backpackers.

Frazier Outfitting operates 40 miles southwest of Creede, Colorado, at the headwaters of the Rio Grande River and surrounded by the Continental Divide. Permitted access includes both the Rio Grande National Forest and the Weminuche Wilderness.

This is a small business specializing in personal, quality, outdoor experience.

"Honesty, integrity and a burning desire to please clients are Sammy's attributes." Barry Iden

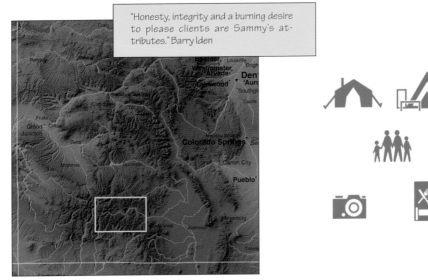

# Granite Creek Guest Ranch

## Carl and Nessie Zitlau

P.O. Box 340 • Ririe, ID 83443
phone: (208) 538-7140 • fax: (208) 538-7876

Granite Creek Guest Ranch is one of the most scenic cattle ranches in the West. Nestled against the border of Caribou National Forest, it is comprised of about 2,600 acres of mountainous timber and range land, and 400 acres of farm land. The Zitlau family has raised cattle here since the early 1900s.

It is a "real" working cattle ranch with just the right touch of civilization. Families, couples and singles of all ages and horse skills have a terrific time.

Ranch activities include wonderful home-cooked meals, rustic cabins with private baths, fishing in the private lake, a variety of terrain for great trail riding, and our specialty — cattle drives and roundups.

"My 16 year old son enjoyed this more than anything else we've ever done, and we've done a lot" Kathy Crowley

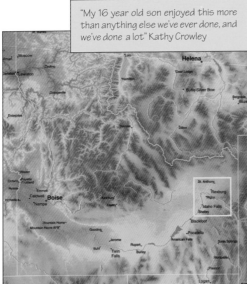

GRANITE CREEK
GUEST RANCH

# Hargrave Cattle and Guest Ranch

**Leo and Ellen Hargrave**

300 Thompson River Rd. • Marion, MT 59925
phone: (406) 858-2284 • fax: (406) 858-2444
email: hargrave@digisys.net • www.hargraveranch.com

Live the legend on a historic 87,000 acre working ranch. National forest surrounds our mountain valley jewel. Choose your adventure, whether it's many hours in the saddle or a leisurely ride to check cattle. Join us in spring for calving and herd-check riding. Join summer drives to the range or fall roundups. Count stars on a campout by pristine lake and peaks. Day trips to spectacular Glacier National Park or National Bison Range.

Skeet and target shooting, archery, lake canoeing, cowboy campfire sing-a-longs, pool games in the horse barn museum, and private meadow fishing. On-site massage therapist arranged.

Outfitted fly fishing float trips, whitewater rafting, guided fall hunting, winter cross country skiing and holiday cabins. Grandma's cooking, delightful lodging, and caring are our standards.

We were Outfitters on the Great Montana Cattle Drive and are committed to sharing that Western Spirit with our guests.

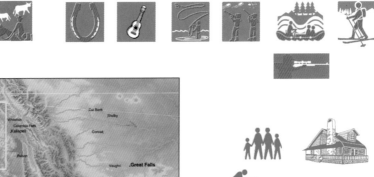

"It was a dream come true - reality was 1,000 times better than the dream. It's the adventure of a lifetime!!!" Virginia Wiscovich

# Hartley Guest Ranch

**Doris and Ray Hartley**

HCR 73, Box 55 • Roy, NM 87743

phone: (800) OUR-DUDE (687-3833) • (505) 673-2245 • fax: (505) 673-2216

email: rhart@etsc.net • www.duderanch.org/hartley

So, should you have been a cowboy? The Hartley Family invites you to experience and enjoy our working cattle ranch, nestled in the breathtaking beauty of New Mexico.

Explore 200 miles of trails that circle the rims of redrock canyons and wind through forest of juniper, oak and pine by horseback or ATV. Other ranch activities: cattle working, branding, campouts, fishing, campfires, and hiking. Discover ancient Indian sites, dinosaur bones, and unusual geological formations located on the ranch. Rafting trips and day trips to enchanting Santa Fe and Taos.

Delicious home-cooked meals are served family-style in the dining room or cooked outdoors over an open fire. Transportation from Albuquerque.

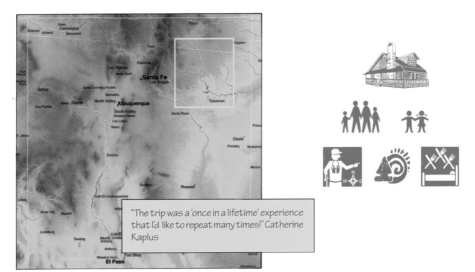

"The trip was a 'once in a lifetime' experience that I'd like to repeat many times!" Catherine Kaplus

Hartley Guest Ranch

# Hidden Hollow Hideaway

## Kelly and Jill Flynn

P.O. Box 233 • Townsend, MT 59644
phone: (406) 266-3322

Our ranch — more than 20,000 acres of mountains, creeks, meadows, and forests — is known as Hidden Hollow Ranch, home of the Hideaway. On our northern ranch, the Hideaway nestles alongside a meandering stream under towering willow trees. Two acres of landscaped lawns surround the old lodge, log cabin, small cabin and new main lodge. The cabins are rustic but very comfortable. All have showers, electricity, and wood stoves. Three home-cooked meals are served daily.

Ride horses on a ridge overlooking miles of mountains and meadows. Pan for gold alongside a rushing mountain stream. Take an "off the beaten path" four-wheel-drive tour. Sit around a campfire or enjoy a barbecue. Hike through wildflower-blazing meadows. Fish at a nearby creek or one of our ranch ponds. Pitch in on some of the ranch work, or just sit back and enjoy the peace and solitude.

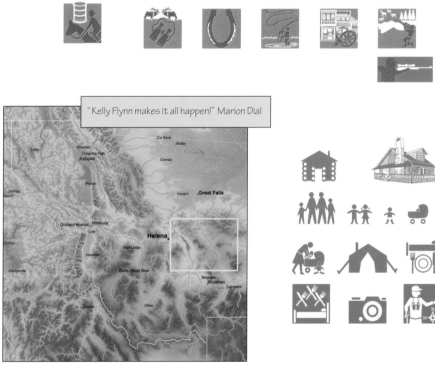

" Kelly Flynn makes it all happen!" Marion Dial

# Iron Wheel Ranch

### John & Sherry Cargill
40 Cedar Hills Road • Whitehall, MT 59759
phone/fax: (406) 494-2960 • mobile: (406) 491-2960

Recreation is a full-time job for our family run business. We offer all forms of summer recreation for everyone. Trail rides for individuals or groups up to 8, hourly or full-day trips with cookouts.

Our youth camps for children 7-15 specialize in teaching children how to handle, saddle, care and ride their horse. Child gets their "own" horse for the entire week. We camp out and children put up their own tent and learn other camping responsibilities.

Blue ribbon rivers are fun for everyone, with many river and fishing option available as well as our private pond.

Our Bed & Breakfast lodge offers many combination vacations including float trips, trail rides, seasonal varmint and big game hunts. On site we have horseshoe pits, volleyball net, BBQ's, fire rings and a creek. We are located near the Continental Divide and easily accessible.

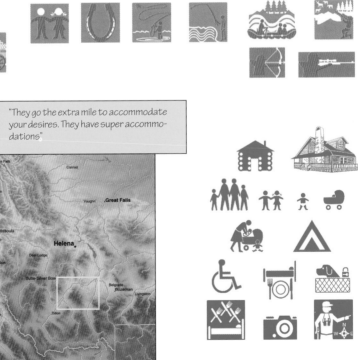

"They go the extra mile to accommodate your desires. They have super accommodations"

# John Henry Lee Outfitters, Inc.

## John Lee

Box 8368 • Jackson, WY 83001
phone: (800) 352-2576 • (307) 733-9441 • fax: (307) 733-1403

Travel by horseback into Yellowstone National Park or the Bridger Teton Wilderness. Experience the spirit of adventure and exploration as you venture into a remote and secluded area for spectacular fishing and scenery.

Photography and scenic trips move into the beautiful and breathtaking scenery of the high mountain country. There are abundant fields of wildflowers, lush alpine meadows, and lodgepole pine forests. This wilderness area offers you excellent opportunities to see a variety of wildlife in their natural habitat. You will enjoy the solitude and tranquil environment of the pristine wilderness.

We maintain a clean and comfortable camp. All of our equipment and horses are in excellent shape. Our mountain-wise horses can accommodate even the most novice rider.

Hearty delicious meals are served by the campfire where the stories get better and better as the stars twinkle the night away.

"We can honestly say we enjoyed every minute of each trip and would highly recommend this outfitter to anyone who loves the outdoors, mountains, horses and adventures!" Jeani Smith

John Henry Lee
Outfitters, Inc.

# K Bar Z Guest Ranch & Outfitters

## Dave Segall and Dawna Barnett

P.O. Box 2167 • Cody, WY 82414
phone: (307) 587-4410 • fax: (307) 527-4605

K Bar Z Guest Ranch is nestled between the Beartooth and Absaroka mountain ranges, along the Chief Joseph Scenic Highway.

This guest ranch has everything you need to make your Wyoming vacation a trip to remember. Whether it is hiking a mountain trail, horseback riding through pristine meadows or fishing the famous Clarks Fork River for native cutthroat.

For the more adventurous, pack trips into the wilderness are available. Experienced guides and gentle horses will take you into the heart of the Rockies where you can see elk, deer, moose, mountain goat and even grizzly bear.

While at the ranch you will enjoy rustic cabins, family-style meals and good old western hospitality.

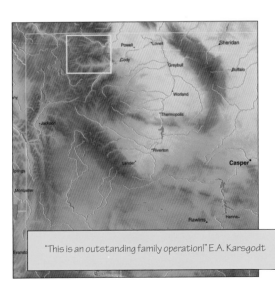

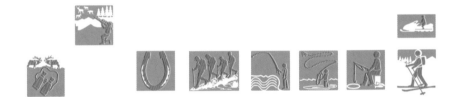

"This is an outstanding family operation!" E.A. Karsgodt

# K BAR Z
## GUEST RANCH
## & OUTFITTERS

# Lakeview Resort and Outfitters

## Dan and Michelle Murphy

Box 1000 • Lake City, CO 81235
phone: (800) 456-0170 • (970) 944-2401 • fax: (970) 641-5952 * Lic. # 939

The Lakeview Resort is located on the shores of Lake San Cristobal, in many folks' opinion, the most beautiful lake in Colorado.

We have lodge rooms, spacious suites and quaint cabins with woodburning fireplaces or stoves.

The Lakeview Resort offers a family atmosphere with many adventurous activities. We offer fishing boats, family pontoon boats and new Jeeps for rent. Expert guided fishing is available on the lake.

Exciting horseback activities are also available, with two-hour rides, sunset supper rides, all-day historic or fishing rides and overnight pack trips.

We have the most complete conference center facility in the Lake City area.

"I cannot praise them enough. They went above and beyond the call of duty to make my experience a treasured memory."

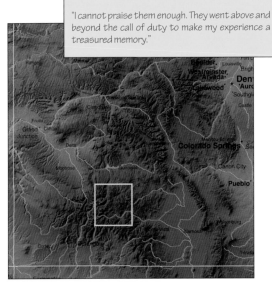

# Lozier's Box "R" Ranch

**Levi M. Lozier**

Box 100-PBYB • Cora, WY 82925
phone: (800) 822-8466 • (307) 367-4868 • fax: (307) 367-6260

*Experience the True West and Live that Life-Long Dream.*
Come join the Lozier's 100 year tradition on one of
Wyoming's finest working cattle/horse guest ranches.

Nestled between two lakes, the Box "R" borders the
Bridger National Forest, with 840,000 acres to ride and
roam. Ride from 7,500 to 11,000 feet elevation or move
25-1,000 head of cattle on our adults-only Lonesome
Dove Cattle drives.

To ensure you of a top-notch riding vacation, the ranch
has 100 head of finely trained horses/mules and boasts a
4-to-1 horse/guest ratio.

Unlimited riding with liberties and freedoms not found
on other guest ranches.

"The Lozier family is wonderful, warm, welcoming and
a joy to 'reacquaint' with each year" Erin L. Burke

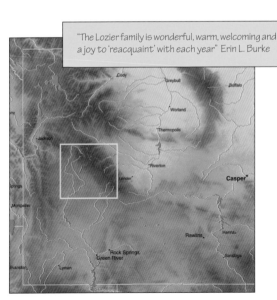

LOZIER'S

R RANCH

CORA, WYOMING

# Maynard Ranch

**Perry and Brenda Hunsaker • Billy and Nora Maynard**

19831 E Warner Rd. • Higley, AZ 85236

phone: (602) 988-9654 • fax: (602) 988-3292

You're invited to spend some time at an authentic New Mexico cattle and guest ranch. Roam the mountains and valleys where some of the West's most famous outlaws stirred up havoc, including Billy the Kid, and Butch Cassidy.

Set on nearly 3,000 acres and surrounded by National Forest with towering ponderosa pines, oak thickets and lush meadows. Enjoy horseback riding through the forests or spend time in the saddle with cowboys working cattle. Play cowboy golf, take a hayride, go fishing or just sit back and unwind.

Daytrips available to nearby Indian ruins and archaeological sites. Spend evenings around the campfire listening to a cowboy poet or enjoy the star-filled sky and Milky Way. We offer a great kids' program.

The ranch has comfortable accommodations perfect for family reunions and corporate retreats. Hearty meals are served family-style.

"The food was delicious, and the coffee pot was always going. A total warm & relaxing experience. Can't wait to return to Maynard Ranch!" Carol Jordan

# M a y n a r d   R a n c h

# Monture Face Outfitters

## Tom Ide and Valerie Call

Box 27 • Greenough, MT 59836
phone: (888) 420-5768 • phone/fax: (406) 244-5763

Monture Face Outfitters is your host to Montana's "Bob Marshall Wilderness," nearly 1.5 million acres of pristine beauty in the heart of the Rocky Mountains.

Travel into and through the wilderness on top-notch horses and mules. Pack trips are flexible, from three days to a high adventure eight-day roving experience. Abundant wildflowers and wildlife provide photo opportunities at every bend of the trail, and the trout fishing is outstanding. Only the highest quality ingredients are used in the gourmet wilderness kitchen. Build campfires at night and immerse yourself in a sea of stars.

Owner Tom Ide, son Tim, and Valerie Call have one ultimate goal; to share the magic of wilderness. Knowledgeable, experienced and quality -oriented.

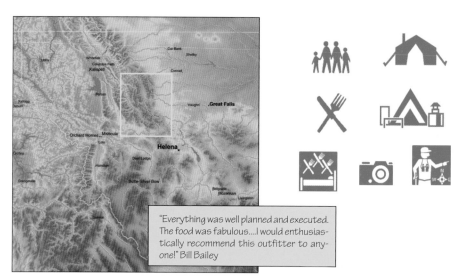

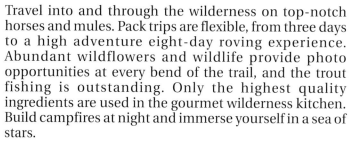

"Everything was well planned and executed. The food was fabulous....I would enthusiastically recommend this outfitter to anyone!" Bill Bailey

**Monture Face Outfitters**

# Nine Quarter Guest Ranch

## Kim and Kelly Kelsey

5000 Taylor Fork Rd. • Gallatin Gateway, MT 59730
phone: (406) 995-4276 (ranch) • (406) 586-4972 (home)

From a secluded valley overlooking Yellowstone National Park, the Kelsey's have been hosting guests for more than 50 years. The ranch-raised herd of 120 Appaloosa horses will take you through pine forests, over mountain streams and across wildflower-strewn meadows.

Fun at the Nine Quarter includes children with a kiddie wrangler and a ranch babysitter. Among the weekly activities are square dances, hay rides, wildlife lectures and softball games. Other pastimes include hiking, photography or just relaxing on your porch to the cry of a coyote.

The Taylor Fork, a fine trout stream, flows through the ranch. With a trout pond and ranch guide at your side, you will soon be hooked on fishing these famous headwaters of the Missouri River.

"Our vacation in Montana has become a family tradition, to go back to 'the ranch, our ranch' Nine Quarter Circle Ranch, Gallatin Gateway, Montana"
Mr. & Mrs. Brian Hensley

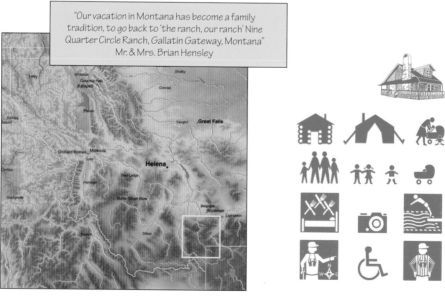

# Rich Ranch

## Jack and Belinda Rich

P.O. Box 495 • Seeley Lake, MT 59868
phone: (406) 677-2317 • fax: (406) 677-3530
email: richranch@montana.com • www.richranch.com

Summer ranch vacations are available from May through September. While at the ranch you will enjoy quiet country living. The lodge and cabins are nestled in the trees overlooking a large natural meadow with a scenic backdrop of majestic mountains. We are surrounded by more than one million acres of state and national forests.

Horseback riding is the main activity. Each guest is fitted to a saddle and we carefully choose a horse suited to your ability.

Do you prefer a leisurely morning ride through the meadows and rolling hills, a high adventure trip to the top of the mountain, or maybe some time to work on your horsemanship skills in our outdoor arena? The choice is yours.

Quality fishing for all levels, beginner to expert, is available in nearby lakes, streams and rivers.

"I would have to say our enthusiasm from our trip was infectious enough that other couples and an acquaintant asked to go along on our next trip!" John L. Trudel

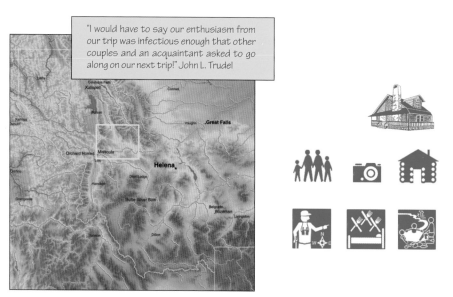

# RICH RANCH

# San Juan Outfitting

## Tom and Cheri Van Soelen

186 County Rd. 228 • Durango, CO 81301
phone: (970) 259-6259 • fax: (970) 259-2652
email: sjo@frontier.net • www.subee.com/sjo/ • Lic. # 997

San Juan Outfitting specializes in classic western horse pack trips. We offer only high-quality trips catering to small groups.

Our spring pack trips take you into the ruins of the ancients (Anasazi Indians) for three to four days. Summer and fall pack trips for fishing, photography and relaxing takes you into the heart of the Weminuche Wilderness to a base camp just below the Continental Divide at an elevation of 10,300 feet. Our high country lake trip travels portions of the Divide while fishing some of the high lakes.

The ultimate adventure is our Continental Divide ride. We travel approximately 100 miles of the Divide at an average elevation of 12,500 feet.

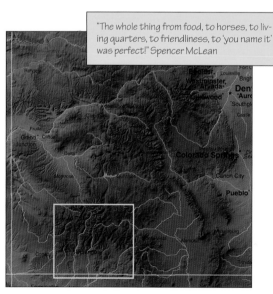

"The whole thing from food, to horses, to living quarters, to friendliness, to 'you name it' was perfect!" Spencer McLean

# San Juan Outfitting

# Schmittel Packing & Outfitting

## David and Verna Schmittel

15206 Hwy. 285 • Saguache, CO 81149
phone: (719) 655-2722 • Lic. # 344

Schmittel Packing and Outfitting has provided exciting, high-quality pack trips for 30 years in the wilderness and non-wilderness areas of the San Juan/Rio Grande and Gunnison National Forests, located in "America's Switzerland" of southwestern Colorado.

The area provides a spectacular opportunity to enjoy excellent trail horses, abundant and varied wildlife, unique riding experiences and excellent meals. Dave and Verna have hosted guests with varied riding abilities from every state and many foreign countries.

No one has to be a seasoned rider to enjoy the gorgeous scenery and good company. Each trip is different, allowing guests to visit this magnificent region again and again.

Member of Colorado Outfitters Association, Rio Grande Chapter of the Colorado Outfitters Association, and People for the West.

"It is a privilege and a pleasure to horsepack with Dave and Verna Schmittel, and the finest string of pack horses I have ever experienced" Ronald F. Cox

# Skyline Guest Ranch

**Sheila and Mike Farny**

PO Box 67 • Telluride, CO 81435

phone: (888) 754-1126 • (970) 728-3757 • fax: (970) 728-6728

email: skyline-ranch@toski.com

A warm western welcome awaits you, your family and friends at Skyline Guest Ranch. We are committed to sharing with you a special spirit we call "Mountain Joy." Camaraderie flourishes, adventures are shared and there is time for special moments in surroundings of unsurpassed beauty and peace.

You may choose to spend your holiday in one of our ten lodge rooms, each with private bath, or in one of our housekeeping cabins which sleep from two to six people. Skyline is located three miles from the Telluride ski area where you will find some of the finest, uncrowded slopes in the West.

In winter, we offer sleigh rides, cross country skiing, and fine dining. In summer you will enjoy riding one of our horses, fishing in our three trout-filled lakes or riding a mountain bike to an abandoned ghost town.

"..the Farny's and Skyline staff are definitely a cut above their competition!
Elaine & Doug Moore

SKYLINE
GUEST RANCH

# White Tail Ranch/WTR Outfitters, Inc.

## Jack and Karen Hooker

520 Cooper Lake Rd. • Ovando, MT 59854
phone: (888) WTR-5666 • phone/fax: (406) 793-5666
email: wtroutfitters@montana.com • www.recworld.com/wtro

WTR Outfitters has been specializing in summer horse pack trips since 1940.

Join Karen and Jack Hooker on the ride of a lifetime into the Bob Marshall, Great Bear and Scapegoat Wilderness areas.

Hike across fields splashed with the bright blues, reds and yellows of alpine flowers. Ride along the Chinese Wall, a 1,500 foot sheer cliff. Fish for native cutthroat trout in remote, gin-clear streams. Photograph deer, elk, and perhaps even a grizzly.

Trips can be customized to suit your wishes or you can join one of our scheduled trips.

"In my opinion the Hookers' are the very top of their profession!" John & Rose Marie McGoldrick

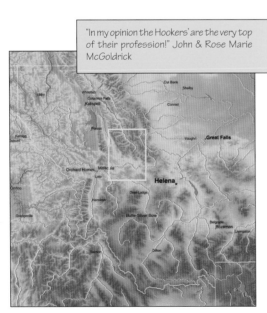

# APPENDIX

This is the compete list of the outdoor professionals and businesses operating in the Rocky Mountain Region we contacted during the compilation of our book.

We invited them to participate in our survey by simply sending us their complete client list.

Some replied prizing our idea, but still decided not to participate in our survey. Their main concern was the confidentiality of their client list. We truly respect this position, but we hope to have proven our honest and serious effort. We are sure they will join us in the next edition.

Some participated by sending their client list, but did not qualify for publication. In some cases because of a low score, and in other instances because of an insufficient number of questionnaires returned by their clients.

The names of the outdoor professionals who have qualified by receiving an A rating from their past clients are **bolded** in the Appendix.

## COLORADO

Bob Anderson
Gregory John Anderson
Barbara A. Baird
Russell Behrman
Lynn Robert Belleville
Dennis Betz
Frank Blackshere Jr.
Jim Bradwell
Kent Calhoun
Darrell W. Camilletti
Edwin D. Coleman
Rodney S. Cook
Rodney S. Cook
James R. DeKam
Theodore Dooley
Bobby Ray Farmer
Gerald Field
Bruce Fotopulos
Pauline "PS" Freberg
Dennis Fredrickson
Joseph C. Fyvie
Joseph Fyvie
L. Dean Gent
Albert Goode
Ivan Green
Ivan Green
Art Gurule
Gus Halandras
David & Russell Hardagine
Ronald Hartong
Jonh Hatlem
Melvin Hawkins
Thomas Herrera
Tim Kostur & Tim Hiett
David Joseph Johnson
Malcolm Carter Jolley, Jr.
James L. Jones
James Jones
Stephen R. Jusseaume
John M. Kane
Richard A. Lillard
Mike W. Luark
Larry Mann
Dean Mantle
John L. Markham
Denise Mead
Hal Mecham
William A. Montieth
David P. Morlan
Dan Newman
M. Don Oliver

Kenneth G. Osborn
Glen Papez
Wayne Pennell
Andy Peroulis
Robert Cole Proctor
Rick L. Quinn
De Lyle Rowley
Jim W. Schaffer
Thomas G. Shankster
Nick D. Speicher & Sam Smith
James G. Snyder
Charlie Stockstill
Jay Templeton
Jack E. Timmer Jr.
James J. Tresch
Mark Turner
Steve Whinnery
Bruce A. White
Bruce White
James T. Wilcox
Lyle Willmarth
Ronny Yeager
#1 Call For Family Adventure & N Outfitters, Inc.
Timothy Henley McCollum
2V Outfitters, LTD.
Stephen Greenway
**4 + 2 T Ranch**
**Craig T. Tomke**
4 UR Ranch, Inc.
Rock Swenson
5 Springs Ranch Guide & Outfitter
Louis Rabin
7-M Guide Service
Seven Mazzone
7M Guide Service
Seven Mazzone
7W Guest Ranch
Russ Papke
A J Gamebirds
A Wanderlust Adventure
Patrick Legel
Action Adventures
Adams Lodge
Ron Hilkey
Adventure Bound Inc.,River Exp.
Tom & Robin Kleinschnitz
Adventure Experiences, Inc.
Tim Kempfe
Agape Outfitters & Guide Service
Donna & Wayne Peck

AJ's Gun Club
Anthony J. Kippes
Al's Outfitting
Allen J. Roberts
Alameno Outfitting & Guide Service
Frank Alameno
Alaska Wildland
William Fischer
Alexander Outfitters
Dave & Kerry Alexander
Alkali Outfitters
Jerry Satterfield
All Seasons Ranch
M. Bruce Cottrell
Allen's Guide Service
Don Allen
Almont Outfitters, Inc./Scenic River
Matthew L. Brown
Alpine Angling & Adventure Travel
Anthony Fotopulos & Bruce Stolbach
Alpine Outfitters
Chris Cassidy
Altenbern Hunting
Clay A. Altenbern
American Outfitters
James M. Knight
American Rafting/Lakota River Guides
Darryl Bangert
American West Safaris & Flying Eagle Outfitters
Mark Anderson
Anasazi Angler
Anderson's Guide Service
Daniel J. Anderson
Andy Julius Outfitter & Guide
Leal Andrew Julius
Angler's Covey, Inc.
Kent A. Brekke
Angler's Covey, Inc.
Kent & Kurt Brekke
Apache Park Ranches
Erna Sears
Archery Unlimited Outfitters
Marshall Ledford
Archery Unlimited Outfitters
Marshall Ledford
Arkansas River Fly Shop
Rodney A. Patch
Arkansas River Tours

Robert Hamel/Margie Geurs
Aspen Canyon Ranch
David Lewis & Steven Roderick
Aspen Canyon Ranch, LLC
Steven Roderick
Aspen Lodge @ Estes Park
Tim Resch
Aspen Outfitting Co., Ltd.
Jonathan F. Hollinger
Aspen Trout Guide & Outfitter, Inc.
Scott Alan Nichols
Aspen Wilderness Outfitters, Ltd.
Tim McFlynn
Astraddle A Saddle Inc.
Gary Bramwell
Astraddle A Saddle, Inc.
Gary Bramwell
Avalanche Outfitters
Mike Schilling
B & B Outfitters of Durango
Robert C. Fertsch
B & J Hunting Camp
Robert W. Wells
B & J Hunting Camp
Robert W. Wells
B & W Guide Service
Lawrence Beagley
B 4 J Outfitters
Robert Jeffreys Jr.
B R Rhyne Guide & Outfitting
Bruce L. Rhyne
Back Country Guides & Outfitters
William A. Yeagher
Backcountry Angler
Backcountry Outfitter, Inc.
David L. Guilliams, Sr.
Backcountry Outfitters
Bill Yeagher
Backcountry Outfitters, Inc.
David & Nancy Guilliams
Backcounty Angler
Gregg S. Jorgensen
Badger Basin Outfitters
Randy E. Tinlge
Badger Creek Guide & Outfitter
Tim R. Hamilton
Badger Creek Guide & Outfitter
Tim Hamilton
Badger Creek Outfitter

Joe E. Nelson
Bang Away Gun Club & Kennels
Bar Diamond Ranch/Ferrier Outfitters
Dellis Ferrier
Bar Lazy J Guest Ranch
Jerry & Cheri Helmicki
Bar Lazy L Family, Inc.
Gary Yeager
Bar T Outfitters
Phillip & Joanne Talmadage Mark
Bar X Bar
Clayton Stephenson
Bar Z X Ranch & Lodge
Dean Lampton
Barr Lake Hunting Club
Barrett Park Outfitters
Jack Steenbergen
Basin Outfitters
Ken E. Wissel
Basin Outfitters
Kenneth E. Wissel
Beacon Landing Motel & Marina
David A. & Betty J. McCloskey
Bear Basin Ranch
Gary Ziegler
Bear Cat Outfitters
Seth E. Peters
Bear Creek Ranch
Edward Wintz
Bear Paw Outfitters
Sam & Susan Ray
Bearcat Outfitters
Seth Peters
Beaten Path Outfitters
Jeffery Wayne Baylor
Beaver Canyon Guide & Outfitter
Greg Pink
Beaver Creek Stables
Steve Bruce Jones
**Beaver Meadows Resort Ranch**
North Fork Financial Corp.
Beaver Mountain Outfitters
C. Duain Morton
Beaver Mountain Outfitters
Duain Morton
Beaver Valley Ranch
Michael Cosby
Behram Outfitting
Russell Behrman
Best Guide & Outfitters
Donald L. Ankrum
Big Bones Unlimited/Catspaw Ranch
Dennis E. Schutz
Big Cimarron Outfitter
Matt Wade Munyon
Big Cimarron Outfitters
Matt or Ken Munyon
Big Creek Reserve
John E. Sandelin
Big Game Hunts, LLC
Ralph A. Babish
Big Horn Outfitters
Lester Dean Hawkins
Big Horn Outfitters
R. Vernon Mann
Big Mountain Outfitters
Sam Potter
Big Rack Outfitters
Eric Lee Hamilton
Big Rack Outfitters
Eric Lee Hamilton
Big Timbers Guest Ranch Inc.
Brad Nothnagel & Dean Wagner
Bighorn Outfitting
Dan C. Cooper & Dan Moyer

**Bill Dvorak's Kayaking & Rafting Expeditions**
Bill Law Guide Service
Bill Law
Black Elk Guides & Outfitters
Black Elk Outfitters, LTD
Dell H. Bean
Black Mesa Lodge
Tom McLeod
Black Mesa Lodge
Tom McLeod
Black Mountain Invest. Ltd.
Nowell R. May
Black Timber Outfitters
Carrol M. Johnson & Kent Fischer
Black Timber Outfitters
Kent Fischer & Carroll Johnson
Blanco River Outfitters
Carl Bentley
Blays Western Colorado Outfitters
Gordon Blay
Blazing Adventures
Bob Harris
Blue Creek Outfitters
Scott Dillon
Blue Mountain Outfitters
Shawn M. Bentley
Blue Quill Angler
Blue Quill Anglers, Inc.
Mark A. Harrington
Bookcliff Outfitters
Bruce Nay
Brady Guide Service
Jeffrey L. Brady
Breckenridge Outfitters
Beane, Davis & Beane Crosby
Breckenridge Outfitters Inc.
Paul H. Brooks
Broadacres Guest Ranch
Broken Antler Outfitters
Jacob H. Kauffman
Broken Spoke Ranch
Clifford Davis
Browner's Guide Service
Raymond G. Kitson/Hank Bevington
Brush Creek Outfitters Inc.
Dennis Russell Grieve
Brushbusters Inc/B & B Outfitters of Durango
Robert Fertsch
Bruton's Guide Service
C. Warren Bruton
Bryce Outfitting
Jim Bryce
BSL Enterprises
Scott Taylor
BSL Enterprises
Scott Taylor
Buck's Livery Inc.
Ben & Mindy Breed
Buck Ridge Outfitters
Ed Ilhareguy
Bucks Livery, Inc.
Ben Breed
Buckskin Trails
Glenn W. Pritchard
Bud Flowers Guide & Outfitters
Bud Flowers
Buffalo Creek Outfitters, Inc.
Mike L. Prescott
Buffalo Horn Ranch, Inc.
James H. Walma
Buford Guide Service
Tom Tucker
Buggywhip's Fish & Float Service
Jim Blackburn
Bugle Masters
Troy J. Hicks

Buglin' Bill Outfitters
Bill Allen
Bull's Eye Outfitters Inc.
Warren R. Allmon
Bull Basin Guides & Outfitters
Dean Billington
Bull Mountain Outfitters
Harry Wayne Garver
Bull Mountain Outfitters, Inc.
Vicki L. Hale
Burton's Guide Service
Clyde Warren Bruton
C & D Outdoors
Don Polzin
C & M Outfitters
Marcus Walker
Cabin Creek Outfitters
Tony Tingle
Cache Creek Outfitters
Jim DeKam
Cadwell Outfitters
Curtis Cadwell
Calhoun Guide & Outfitting
Jay Jefferson & Bob Stokes
Camilletti and Son's Inc.
Edward Camilletti
Cannibal Outdoors
Jack & Leslie Nichols
Canyon Creek Outfitter
Frank Fraser
Canyon Marine Whitewater Exp.
Gregory Wright Felt
Capitol Peak Outfitters
Steve & Sandy Rieser
Capitol Peak Outfitters, Inc.
Steve Rieser
Cedar Breaks Guides & Outfitters
Monte Lew Miller
Cedar Mountain Guide Service
Daniel L. Weber
Chad Hopwood Construction
Chad Hopwood
Chair Mountain Stables
Tom Mainer III
Challenge Outfitters
David L. Eider
Challenge Outfitters
David Eider
Challenge Outfitters
Mike Martindale
Champion Outfitters
Dale V. Sundblom
Chaparral Park General Store
Karen Johnston
Cherokee Outfitters
Chuck Baker
Cherokee Park Ranch
Cherokee Trading Post & Outfitters
David Slater
Chris Loncarich Guide Service
Chris Loncarich
Chuck Davies Guide Service, Inc.
Chuck & Mark Davies
Chuck Davies Guide Service, Inc.
Mark Davies
Chuck McGuire Flyfishing
Charles D. McGuire
Chuit River Lodge
Jeffrey Hauck
Cimarron Ridge/High Country Outfitters
Thomas L. Bailey
Circle Bar Outfitting
Larry Allen
Circle Four Hunting
Thomas I. & Thomas R. Lindley
Circle K Ranch Outfitters
Al & John Cannon

Cirrus Corporation
Gary White
Coal Basin Partners
Coal Creek Outfitting
Rod Black
Collegiate Peaks Outfitters
David Douty
Colorado's Mountain West Outfitting Co.
Wlly Pete Georgiou
Colorado Angler
Rhonda D. Sapp
Colorado Back Country Outfitters
Alan Bishop
Colorado Big Game Connections, Inc.
Robert Gee
Colorado Big Game Outfitter
Kenneth Osborn
Colorado Blue Outfitters
David G. Hargadine
Colorado Diamond D Outfitters
Thomas D. Dunn
Colorado Elite
John D. Verzuh
Colorado Fishing Adventures
Gary J. Willmart
Colorado Fishing Guides
Colorado Guest Ranch
Larry & Elaine Mautz
Colorado High Country Outfitters
Steven Weaver
Colorado High Couny Outfitters
The Hatlees
Colorado High Guide Service
Dennis Bergstad & Cade Benson
Colorado Hunting Adventures
Brad & Terry Knotts
Colorado Mule Deer
Linda L. Strong
Colorado Outfitters, Inc.
Kelly Brooks
Colorado Pheasant Association
Colorado Riff Raft
Peter Hicks
Colorado River Guides, Inc.
Brenda D. Worley
Colorado River Runs, Inc.
Joe Kelso
Colorado Trail Riders & Outfitters
Doug Flowers
Colorado Trails Ranch
Robin Williams
Colorado Trophies
Jay Scott
Colorado Trophies
Jay Scott
Colorado Trophy Guides
Jim Stehle
Colorado Trophy Guides
John & Jim Stehle
Colorado Wilderness Safaris, Inc.
Paul E. Mitzel, Jr.
Columbine Outfitters
Dan Bell
Columbine Outfitters, LLC
Greg Ward
Comanche Wilderness Outfitters, Inc.
Scott A. Limmer
Conejos River Outfitters
Walter Heady Jr.
Cooper's Outfitting & Guide Service
Paul Cooper & Mark Chiono
Cottonwood Meadows Guide

Service
Randy P. Keys
Cougar Mountain, Inc.
Si H. Woodruff
Coulter Lake Guest Ranch Inc.
C. Norman Benzinger
Cowboy Camp Outfitters Inc.
Robert Port
Craig Outfitting Servic
Philip S. Craig
Crampton Mountain Outfitters
Roger Rupp
Crawford Ranch
Gayle R. Crawford
Creative Outdoor Sprts
Frank E. Meek
CST Hunting Service, Inc.
Chris E. Maneotis
Culbreath Cattle Co.
Grady Culbreath
D & G Horses
Dale Coombs
D & S Guide & Outfitter
Dennis E. Rodebaugh
DAL Outfitters, Inc.
David Lowry
Dale Haskins Hunting
Dale Haskins
Dan's Fly Shop
Dan Hall
Dan Hughes Outfitting &
Guides
Dan Hughes
Daniel J. Humphrey Guides
Daniel J. Humphrey
Dave Parri's Outfitting & Guide
Service
David Parri
Dave Yost Outfitters
Merrilee Yost
Dawson Guide & Outfitters
Service
Douglas & Steven Dawson
Dee Norell Ranch
Franklin Dee Norell
Deep Creek Outfitters
Darla Ranwick Cluster
Deer Valley Ranch
Harold Lee DeWalt
Del's Triangle 3 Ranch
Ray Heid
Devil's Thumb Fly Fishing Adv.
Center
Devils Thumb Ranch Resort
Inc.
Barry John Gordon
Diamond-D-Ranch &
Outfitters
Obbie L Dickey
Diamond D Bar Ranch
Obbie & Willa Lee Dickey
Diamond Hitch Stables &
Outfitting
Joe Fahrion
Diamond Lodge Guest Ranch
C. Steve Paul
Diamond M Outfitters
Bob Martin
Diamond S Ranch
Mike Walck
Diamond X Bar Outfitting
Robert M. Campbell
Dick Pennington Guide
Service, Ltd.
Alan & Dick Pennington
Dick Piffer Guide & Outfitter
Richard Piffer
Dilley's Guide Service
Dale Dilley
Discount Fishing Tackle, Inc.
Michael L. Gray
Dog Gone Outfitters
Perry Williamson

Don Hawkins Outfitting
Don Hawkins
Double B Ranch Outfitters Inc.
William D. Harmon
Double Diamond Outfitters
Jack Wheeler
Double Dollar Cattle LLC
Wayne Iacovetto
Double H Bar Outfitting
Rick Hummel
Double LJ Outfitters, Inc.
Layne K. Wing
**Dragonfly Anglers / Spadafora
Ranch - Roger Cesario**
Drowsy Water Ranch
Kenneth H. Fosha
Dry Creek Anglers
Charles Grobe
Dry Fork Outfitters
Donald J. Kroese, Jr.
DTD Outfitters
Jack Lowe
Duarte Outfitters
Elmer Duarte
Dunckley Peak Pack Service
William L. Terrill
Duranglers Flies & Supplies
Thomas Knopick
Durango Fly Goods, LLC
Michael J. Stowers
Durango Outfitters, Inc.
Dennis Norton
Durango Rivertrippers
John & Karen Squire
Eagle's Nest Outfitting
Billy Howard
Eagle's Nest Outfitting
Kai Mark Turner
Eagle River Anglers
Robert Nock
Eagle Spirit Outfitters
Miles Hogan
Eagle Spirit Outfitters
Carl Spina
Eagles Nest Outfitting
Billy S. Howard
East Divide Outfitters
Dennis A. Yost
East Divide Outfitters Inc.
Dennis Yost
**Echo Canyon Outfitters**
**David & Kathleen Hampton**
Echo Canyon River
Expeditions
David Burch
Elite Outfitters
Brian Newell
Elk Country Outfitters
David Butterfield
Elk County Outfitters
David Butterfield
Elk Creek Lodge
Chris Lockwood
Elk Creek Marina, Inc.
John Loken
Elk Mountain Guides &
Outfitter
John Pickering
Elk Mountain Outfitter &
Guides
John Pickering
Elk Mountain Outfitters, Inc.
Gerald Seifert
Elk Mountain Ranch
Elk Ridge Adventures
Stephen F. Watwood
Elk River Guest Ranch
Patrick Barrett & William
Hinder
Elk River Guest Ranch
William Hinder
Elkhorn Outfitters Inc.
Richard & Cheryl Dodds

Elkhorn Outfitters, Inc.
Elkhorn Outfitters, Inc.
Richard J. Dodds
Elkshead Guides & Outfitters
John M. Connon
Elkstream Outfitters Inc.
Jon T. Van Ingen
Elktrout Lodge
Marty Cecil
Engine Creek Outfitters
Jim Houghton
Estes Angler
Fantasy Ranch Outfitters, Inc.
James R. Talbot
Farris Outfitters
Paul Farris
Fawn Gulch Outfitters
Dave Hemauer
Ferro's Blue Mesa Outfitters
John Ferro
Finlay River Outfitters
Fly Fishing Outfitters
Flyfisher Guide Service
Reynolds G. Cannon
Flyfishing Durango, Inc.
Bill Leahy
Flyfishing Outfitters, Inc.
William C. Perry
Flyfishing Services, Inc.
Flying Diamond Outfitters,
LLC
John R. Adams
Flying Eagle Outfitters
Mark O. Anderson
Flying Raven Ranch
Matt Redd
Flynn & Sons Outfitters
Delnor F. Flynn
Fossil Ridge Guide Service
Rudy & Deb Rudibaugh
Four Corners Expeditions, Inc.
Reed K. Dils
Four Directions Upland Game
Club
Foutz Outfitting Service
Charles F. Foutz
Fox Creek Adventures Inc.
Cal Junker
Fox I I
**Frazier Outfitting**
**Sammy Frazier**
Fritzlan's Guest Ranch
Calvin Fritzlan Outfitter
Front Range Outfitters
Mark Ross
Front Range Outfitters
Ronald E. Sniff
Frosty Acres Ranch
Doug & Janet Camilletti
Frying Pan Anglers
Ray Clarence Palm
Full Draw Outfitters
Fred Eichler & Don Ward Blye
Chadwick
Gafford Outfitters
Jackie Gafford
**Garvey Bros. Outfitters**
**Doylene & Stan Garvey**
Gateview Ranch
Yosef Lutwak
Geneva Park Outfitters
Terry Sandmeier
Gerald Field Outfitters
Glacier Bay Outfitters
John M. Snyder
Go Fer Broke Gun Club
Golden Gate Outfitters
Randy L. Christensen
Gore Livestock, Inc.
Warren D. Gore
Gorsuch Outfitters
Scott Gorsuch
Gorsuch Outfitters

Scott David Gorsuch
Grand Wapiti Outfitters
Lyle D. Horn
Granite Mountain Lodge Inc.
Susan Glittenberg
Great Divide Outfitters
Dan Newman
Great Scott Adventures
Scott Harkins
Great Western Hunting Camps
Darrell Gilks
Green Acres Ranch
Terry Green
Groundhog Outfitters
James J. Wagoner
Gunnison River Pleasure Park
LeRoy Henry Jagodinski
Gunnison River Telluride
Flyfishers
Henry E. Hotze
Gypsum Creek Outfitters, Ltd.
John Jodrie
H & H Hunting Camp Inc.
Hammer Packing & Meat
Processing
James Hammer
Hanging Horse Ranch Outfitter
Colby Olford
Hansen Cattle Ranch, Inc.
Richard Hansen
Happy Trails Outfitters
Gary L. Calhoun
Hawk Creek Outfitting Co. .
Wesley T. Gore
Hawk Creek Outfitting, Co.
Billy R. Jackson
Heart of the Rockies Outfitters
Wayne E. Spencer
Hermosa Creek Outfitters
Frank Moringstar
Hi Country Outfitters
Richard R. Cooper
High Country Game Birds
High Country Guide &
Outfitter
Paul Irwin
High Country Outfitters, Inc.
Conrad A. Wygant
High Country Outfitters, LLC
Kathy Johnson
High Lonesome Outfitter &
Guides
Thomas W. Bowers
High Lonesome Outfitters
Mark T. Lumpkins
High Lonesome Outfitters of
Colorado
Mark Lumpkins
High Lonesome Ranch
John H. Doden
High Meadow Outfitters
High Meadows Ranch
Dennis Stamp
High Mountain Drifter Guide
High Mountain Drifters, Inc.
Mike Wilson
High Mountain Hookers
High Park Outfitters
Dan Aubuchon
High Plains Outfitters
Donny E. Talton II
High Plateau Outfitters Ltd.
Angela Vannucci
High Trail Outfitters Inc.
Bill Hopp
High West Outfitters
Robert Knowlton & Kim Miller
Highlanders Outfitting &
Guide, Co.
Rhonda Kellerer
Highlands Unlimited Inc.
Geoff Burby
Hill's Guide Service

Clifford & Jancice Hill
Hills Guide Service
Clifford E. & Janice Hill
Hillview Outfitters
Willard Forman
Hillview Outfitters
Willard E. Forman
Holman's High Country Outfitters
Buddy Holman
Honaker Guides & Packers
Pat Honaker
Hook, Line & Leader
David F. Wahl
Horizon River Adventures, Inc.
Vilis J. Zigurs
Horn Fork Guides
Joe Boucher
Horsethief Adventures
Hot "T" Camp
Jack Flowers
Hoza Guide & Outfitting
Tony Hoza
Hubbard Creek Outfitters & Pack Station
Larry Allen
Hyatt Guides & Outfitters
Bruce Hyatt
Imperial Expeditions
Micheal John Jones
Independent Whitewater
William Block
Indian Peak Outfitters
Ardis M. Wright
Indian Summer Outfitters
Rick House
Inland Drifters, LLC
Kimberly Moore
Iron Nipple Fishing & Hunting Co.
Bob Huffman
IX7 Cattle Ranch & Outfitter
Chris & Wayne Pond
J & B Outfitters
Brad Gray
J & J Guides & Outfitters
John Markham
J & J Outfitters of Colorado, Inc.
Gerald L. Woolsey
J & Ray Colorado High County, Inc.
Ronald Franks
J & V Guides & Outfitters
Glenn Jones & Lonny Vanatta
J Bar B Guiding & Outfitting
James D. Beall
J M L Outfitters
Maggie & Marie Haskett
J.C. Trujillo Guide & Outfitter
J.C. Trujillo
Jackson's Guide & Outfitter Service
Robert Jackson
Jake's Rio Grande Outfitting Service
David J. Powell
Jalmor Sportsmen's Club
Jamie Prather Guide & Outfitters
Jamie Prather
Jeffcoat Outfitters
Danny Jeffcoat
Jerry Craig Guide Service
Jerry Craig
Jim Jarvis' Guide & Outfitting Service
James Howard Jarvis
JML Outfitters
Marguerite M. & Marie Haskett
John's Outfitter & Guide Service
John R. Harmon
JT Outfitters

Jeff Burtard
Judd Cooney Outfitting & Guiding
Judd Cooney
K & D Majestic Outfitters
Daniel S. Ruscetti
K & K Outfitters
Marion Bricker
K & W Outfitters
Drew & Billie Kissire
K.E. Schultz Guide & Outfitting Service
Kurt E. Schultz & Art Gurule
KCV Outdoors
K. Craig Vaughn
Keystone Resort
Phillip Stahl
King's Guide Service
Douglas R. King
King Creek Outfitters
Mike Rodriguez
King of King's Guide Service
Paul Pearson
Kinsley Outfitters
Koo-Sto Wilderness Outfitters
Phillip L. Foster
Kuhns' Guide & Outfitters
Douglas Kuhns
KW Wapiti Outfitters, LLC
John Knoll
L & B Hunting & Guide Service
Larry Herod
L & K Guide Service
Lonnie Edward & Kim Peters
Lake Mancos Ranch
**Lakeview Resort & Outfitters**
**Dan & Michelle Murphy**
Lakota Guides & Outfitters
Bob Littlejohn
Lamicq Guides &  Outfitters Inc
John & Diane Lamicq
Lamicq Guides & Outfitters, Inc.
John & Diane Lamicq
Lancaster Outfitters
Patrick L. Lancaster
Latigo Ranch
James A. Yost
Lazy C2 Bar Ranch
James Kelly Sewell
Lazy F Bar Outfitters
Bill Guerrieri
Lazy FF Outfitters
Kirk A. Ellison
Lazy H Guest Ranch
Karen & Phil Olbert
Lazy Hound Outfitters
Tracey Don Clark - Scott Barnes
Leonard Outfitting
Randy Leonard
Little Big Horn Lodge
Harry L. Ergott, Jr.
Little Cone Outfitters
Roy Hutt
Little Creek Ranch
Alan Baier
Little Grizzly Creek Ranch Inc.
Leo Douglas Sysel
Lobo Outfitters
Dick Ray & Mike Ray
Lodgepole Outfitters
Don Pinnt
**Lone Tom Outfitting**
**Paul Janke**
Loner Guide Service, Inc.
Bradley T. Weinmeister
Lost Creek Guides
Lance Edinger
Lost Creek Guides
Lance D. Edinger
Lost Solar Outfitters, Inc.

Thoma Marucco & Gary Stoaks
Lost Solar, Inc.
Thomas J. Marucco
Lost Valley Ranch
Robert L. Foster
Louisiana Purchase Ranch Outfitters
M. Lee Tingle
Lov Ranch
James William Brennan
Luark Ranch & Outfitters
Pat Edward Luark
Lunney Mountain Outfitters
Brett J. Harvey
M & M Outfitters
Tom and Susan Mikesell
M H M Outfitters
George A. Malarsie
Mad Adventures, Inc.
Roger Hedlund
Mamm Peak Outfitters
Jeff & Dea Mead
Mamm Peaks Outfitters
Jeffrey George Mead
Manhattan Creek Outfitters, Inc.
Linda S. Wright-Winterfeld
Marvine Ranch LLC & Elk Creek Lodge
William Wheeler
Matt Bridges Guide & Outfitting
Matthew Bridges, Jr.
McCombs Hunting Camp, Inc.
Susan M. Phillips
McDonald's Outfitter & Guide Service
W. Harry McDonald
McFly's Trophy Guide Service
William Jordan McStay
Meadows Vega
Tom Cox
Medano Pass Guide & Outfitter
Donny Carr
Medicine Bow Outfitters
Jared Florell
Menoken Wildlife Park
Middle Creek Ranch Company
Roy Rozell
Mika Ag Corp.
R. Doris Karlsson
Mike Murphy Wilderness Exp.
**Mike Wilson's High Mountain Drifters**
**Mild to Wild Rafting**
**Alex & Molly Mickel**
Mill Creek Outfitters
Charles E. Wisecup
Mill Creek Outfitters
Chuck Wisecup
Miller Mountain Lemon Lake
Lawrence R. Miller
Mineral Mountain Guide & Outfitters
John H. & Bobbie Martin
Monarch Guides
Ken Kays Kupilik
Monument Hill Outfitters
Don Polzin
Mountain Angler, Ltd.
Mountain Enterprises
Gary & Robin Edwards
Mountain Man Tours
Greg J. Coln
Mountain Top Ranches
Mary & Bob Roesler
Mountain Trails Outfitters
Butch Rawls
Mountain Waters Rafting, Inc.
Casey Lynch
Mountain West Outfitting, Inc.
Aaron R. Neilson
Mt. Blanca Game Bird & Trout

Bill Binnian
Mule Creek Outfitters
Randy & Brenda Myers
Mule Shoe Guide Servie
Billy Joe Dilley
Myers Hunting Services, Inc.
Donald G. Myers
Natural Adventures Inc.
Thomas E. Tietz
Natural Adventures, Inc.
Thomas E. Tietz
Needle Rock Ranch
Steven Duffy
Noah's Ark Adventure Program Ltd
Chuck Cichowitz
Norm Harder Outfitter
Norm Harder
North Fork Ranch
Dean May
North Park Outfitters
Bob Martin
North Star Ooutfitters, Inc.
Robert F. Moreland
Northwest Colorado Scenic Tours
Charles L. Mead
Nova Guides, Inc.
Steven Jay Pittels
OFC Outfitting
Michel C. Maurello
OK Ranch Outfitters
John Carelli
Old West Outfitters
Randy Messick
Oldland & Uphoff
Reuben G. Oldland
Oswald Cattle Company
Stephen Oswald
Ouray Livery Barn
Howard Lewis Linscott
Outdoor Connections
Nicholas J. Kamzalow
Outward Bound USA
Craig Mackey
Over The Hill Outfitters
John Neely
Oxbow Outfitting Co.
Donald L. DeLise
Oxbow Outfitting Co.
Jonathan J. Feinberg
P.T. Outfitters
Paul E. Menhennett
Pack Country Outfitters
Mike Reid
Pagosa Rafting Outfitters
Wayne Walls
Paragon Guides
Pass Creek Outfitters
Lee Sinclair
Peaceful Valley Lodge & Guest Ranch
Peacock Ranch Outfitters
Darren Peacock
Peregrine Guides & Outfitters Inc.
Jack & Cathy Todoverto
Peregrine Guides & Outfitters, Inc.
John Todoverto
Peregrine River Outfitters
Thomas Klema
Performance Tours, Inc.
Kevin Foley
Peters Hunting Service
Harley & Bonnie
Peters Hunting Service
Harley Peters
**Phil's Bowhunting Adventures**
Phil's Colorado Adventures
Phil Phillips
Picked-By-You, LLC
Maurice Valerio

Picketwire Pheasant & Quail
Piedra Packing & Outfitting
Roger Kleckner
Pierce Brothers Outfitting
William Leon & Howard Pierce
Pikes Peak Outfitters
Gary Jordan
Pines Ranch Partnership
Dean Rusk
Piney River Ranch
Kara Heide
Plateau Creek Outfitters
Joe E. Garcia
Platte River Outfitters
Richard Aldrich
Pollards Ute Lodge
Troy R. Pollard
Pomotawh Naantam Ranch
Jon & Dori Lee
Ponderosa Outfitters
Norman Bruce Ayers
Poudre River Outfitters
Rex L. Schmidt
Powderhorn Guest Ranch
Jim & Bonnie Cook
Powderhorn Outfitters
Vincent Woodrow Tanko
Powderhorn Primitive
Outfitters
Cameron Lewis
Prather Outfitters
Ned & Lyle Prather
Prime Time Hunts
William Malizia
Private Land Outfitters
Travis Rowley
Prof. Big Game Guide &
Outfitters
Jack Cassidy
Proline Excursions Inc.
Paul Howard
Purcell Brothers Outfitting Inc.
Duane & Dale Purcell
Purgatoire Outfitters
Jay Waring
Purnell's Rainbow Inn
David P. Purnell
Purple Sage Outfitters
Linda A. & Wesley W. DuBose
Pyramid Llama Ranch
Ann Patricia & Kevin Copeland
Pyramid Outfitters
Steve Whiteside
Quail Run Hunting Preserve
Quaking Aspen Guides &
Outfitters, Inc.
Dave Mapes
Quarter-Circle Circle Ranch
Quarter Circle Circle Ranch
John Judson
R & J Outfitters
Robert Parker
R & R Hunting
Gary J. Rowley
R & R Ranch
Ralph R. Royster
R & T Gun Club
R.J.'s Greystone Guide &
Outfitting
Ronald Tull Jones
Raftopoulos Ranches
John & Steve Raftopoulos
Rainbow Trout Ranch
Dave & Jane VanBerkum
Ram's Horn Guides &
Outfitters
Alan Vallejo
Ramble House
Ranching for Wildlife
Jarrell Massey
Rapp Guides Service Inc.
Anne & Jerry Rapp
Raven Adventure Trips, Inc.

Art Krizman
Rawhide Adventures
Fred & Rod Ellis
Razor Creek Outfitters
Ron K. Brink
Red Feather Guides &
Outfitters
John Todd Peterson
Red Feather Guides &
Outfitters
Todd Peterson
Red Mountain Guest Ranch
William Ridgeway
Red Mountain Outfitters
Jim & Mary Flynn
Redd Ranches Guide &
Outfitter
Paul David Redd
Redd Ranches Guides &
Outfitters Inc.
David Redd
Rendezvous Outfitters &
Guides
Russ & Cheri Eby
Rendezvous Outfitters &
Guides, LTD
William R. Eby
Renegade Gun Club, Inc.
Rick Edinger & Sons
Rick D. Edinger
Rick Warren Guide & Outfitting
Ricky Warren
Riddle's Custom Service
Jack Riddle
Ridgetrack Guide & Outfitting
Craig & Cathy Krumwiede
Rim Rock Outfitters
Monty G. Elder
Rimrock Guide & Outfitting
Charles Harrington
Rimrock/Little Creek
Alan Baier
Ripple Creek Lodge
Ken Jett
River Runners, Ltd.
Brad Dendler
Rivers Bend Outfitting
Kip Gates
Riverside Anglers
Peter McNeil & Dave Ziegler
Roads Less Traveled
Roaring Fork Anglers
Rock Creek Outfitters
Robert Eugene Thompson
Rocky Mountain Adventures,
Inc.
G. David Costlow
Rocky Mountain Fisherman
Monte G. Andres
Rocky Mountain High Tours
Inc.
Dan Davis
Rocky Mountain Outdoor
Center
Alexandra Waldbart
Rocky Mountain Outfitters
Gary W. Bohochik
Rocky Mountain Outfitters
Colt Ross
Rocky Mountain Ranches
Lawrence J. Bishop
Rocky Mountain Rides
Dave Hemauer
Rocky Mountain Roosters
Rocky Mountain Safaris
Denzel Hartshorn
Rocky Pappas Guides &
Outfitters
Rocky Ridge Hunting Club
Rocky Top Outfitters
Steve Packer & Colorado Buck
Rod & Reel Fly Shop
Edward L. Wagner

Rod Wintz Guide Service/
Wason Ranch
Rod Wintz
Rogers Country
Ron-D-View Ranch &
Outfitting
Ron Pfeffer
Ross & Nelson Outfitters &
Guides
Jim Ross & Joe Nelson
Route to Trout
Anthony Joseph Colaizzi, Jr.
Roy Savage Ranches
Roy E. Savage
Royal Gorge Outfitters
Bill Edrington & Bill Carson
Rudy Steele Guides &
Outfitters, Inc.
Rudy Steele
S & K Outfitting & Guide
Service
Paul E. Gingery & K. Kyle
Revell
Saddle Action
Pam Green
Saddle Mountain Guide
Service
Lawrence Zeldenthuis
Saddle Tramp Outfitters
Thomas Bullock
**Samuelson Outfitters**
**Richard & Cathy Samuelson**
San-Pahgre Outdoor Adven./
Outfitting
Stuart D. Chappell
San Juan Back Country
Delbert & Laura Smith
**San Juan Outfitting**
**Tom & Cheri VanSoelen**
San Juan Ranch Outfitters
Scott MacTiernan
San Pahgre Outdoor
Adventures
Stuart Chappell
Sangre De Cristo Outfitters
Tom & Bill Schulze
Schlegel Ranch Co.
Wesley H. Schlegel
**Schmittel Packing &**
**Outfitting**
**David & Verna Schmittel**
Scoop Lake Outfitters Ltd.
David Suitts
Scott Fly Rod Co.
John Duncan
Seely Hunting
Bruce Seely
Seven Lakes Lodge
Steve Cobb
Shamrock Ranch Outfitters
Bruce Wilson
Shavano Outfitters
Jim E. James
Sherrod Ranch
Donald Lee Sherrod
Silver Fox Outfitters
Kevin Martin & Ronald Roll
Silver Peaks Outfitters
Scott E. Williams
Silver Spur Outfitters
Trent Snyder
Silverado Outfitters, Inc.
Larry Kibel
Singletree Outfitting
Fain D. Richardson
Sky Corral Guest Ranch
Karen O'Connor
**Skyline Guest Ranch**
**Sheila & Mike Farny**
Slater Creek Cattle Company,
Inc.
Larry L. Lyster
Sly Creek Guide & Outfitters

Gary Baysinger
Small World Adventures
Enga Lokey
Snowmass Anglers
Ivan L. Perrin
Snowmass Falls Outfitters
Mat Turnbull
Snowmass Falls Outfitters, LTD
Thomas M. Turnbull
Snowmass Oxbow Outfitting
Bill Lund
Snowmass Stables Inc.
Marlene Christopher
Snowmass Whaitewater, Inc.
Bob Harris
Solomon Creek Outfitter
Nancy Solomon
Sombrero Ranches, Inc.
Rex Ross Walker
Southfork Stables, Inc.
Kimberly Kay Baird
Southpark Outfitters
Max Oertle
Southwest Adventures
Corey Veach
Southwest Adventures Ltd.
Charles Hughes
Space Command US Air Force
Charlie Stockstill
**Spadafora Ranches Lodge**
**Roger Cesario**
Sperry's
Joe Sperry
Spike's Outfitters
Perry Alspaugh
Spirit
Sporthaven Ltd.
Sporting Classics @ the
Broadmoor Resort
Colleen Betzing
Sporting Country Guide
Service
John A. McRoy
Sportsman of Lake City, Inc.
Paul Hudgeons
St. Peter's Fly Shop
Frank Praznik
St. Vrain Angler Stores, Inc.
Dale Darling
Stajduhar Ranches & Outfitting
John & Steven Stajduhar
Star Outfitters
Jeffry J. Corriveau & Dennis R.
Craig
Steamboat Lake Fishing Co.,
Inc.
Hans Berend
Steamboat Lake Outfitters, Inc.
Donald Wayne Markley
Steamboat Stables/Sombrero
Ranches Inc.
Rex Walker
Stetson Ranches LLC
Franklin L. Stetson
Stetson Ranches, LLC
Franklin Stetson
Steward Ranch Outfitters
Laverne Gwaltney
Stillwater Gun Club, Inc.
Mark A. Beam
Stone Creek Outfitters
Bob Helmer & Clay Bassett
Story Creek Outfitters
Frank Menegatti
Straightline Products, Inc.
Larry Mann
Straightline Sports
Summit Guides
Dale K. Fields
Sundown Outfitters
David N. Cordray
Sunrise Outfitters
Leroy & Paul Schroeder

Sunrise Outfitters, Inc.
Leroy F. Schroeder
Sunset Ranch, Inc.
Patsy Wilhelm
Sylvan Dale Ranch
Ann Diaz
T & J Outfitters
Sue Jameson & Walter Tycksen
T Lazy 7 Ranch
Rick Deane
T. Mike Murphy & Sons
T. Mike Murphy
Talaheim Lodge
Tobin Osteen
Tarryall River Ranch
Jimmy & Jeannie Lahrman
Taylor Creek Inc.
William Fitzsimmons
Taylor Creek Ranch
Vic Taylor
Taylor Guide & Outfitters
Lance & Terri Taylor
Tayor Creek, Inc.
William D. Fitzsimmons
Telluride Anglers
Telluride Whitewater, Inc./
Telluride Outside
William C. White
Tenderfoot Outfitter & Guide
Steve & Jim Pike Paul
Teocalli Outfitters
Al & Laura Van Dyke
Texas Creek Outfitters
David M. Butcher
The Craig Wild Bunch, Inc.
Many Funkhouser
The Don K Ranch
The Executive Angler
Kevin Leigh Derks
The Fryingpan River Ranch
James B. Rea
The Gone Fishing Company
Chad Butler
The Gunnison Country Guide
Service
John C. Nelson
The Home Ranch
Ken & Cile Jones
The Mountain Angler
Jackson Streit/John P. Streit
The Outfitter Sporting Goods,
Inc.
Larry Seaman
The Peak Fly Shop
**The Troutfitter**
**Dominique Eymere & Bradley**
**Sorock**
Thompson's High County
Guides & Outfitters
Greg Thompson
Three Rivers Resort &
Outfitting
Mark A. Schumacher
Three String Outfitting &
Guiding
Dennis Clendenning
Thunder River Guides
James K. Boyles, Jr.
Timber Basin Outfitters
Gregory Geelhoed
Timberline Outfitters
Perry Abbott
Timberline Outfitters
Perry B. Abbott
Timberline Outfitters
Douglas Frank Jr.
Timberline Outfitters & Guide
Service
Douglass C. Frank, Jr.
Timberwolf Whitewater
Expeditions
Larry Meek
TN Bar Cattle Co., Inc.

Curtis Kuester
Tom Fritzlan & Family
Tom Fritzlan
Tom Payne Outfitting
Tom Payne
Toneda Outfitters
Ed R. Wiseman
Tony Hoza Guide & Outfitter
Anthony Hoza
Track'em Outfitters
Robert Pedretti & Tracy
Grzeskowiak
Trail Ridge Outdoors
Thomas Clinkenbeard
Trail Skills, Inc.
Robert Getz
Trapper Creek Outfitters
Lloyd C. Thompson
Trappers Lake Lodge
Ross Wheeler
Tri-State Outfitters
Richard Petrini
Triple-O-Outfitters
Larry & Reta Osborn
Triple G Outfitter & Guides Inc.
Daniel Eckert & Alan Echtler
Triple G, Inc.
Paul Alan Echtler
Triple Tree Ranch
Margaret Deutsch
Trophy Class Outfitters
Mike Lawson
Trophy Mountain Outfitters
Dean F. Silva
Trophy Time Outfitters
Sean M. Pond
Troutfitters of Aspen/Guides
West
Gary Hubbell
Tuff Trout Ranch, LLC
David A. Gitlitz
Tumbling River Ranch
Jim & Mary Dale Gordon
Twin Buttes Ranch Outfitters
Steve Titus
Twin Mountain
W.A. Roesch
Two Rivers Guest Ranch
Uncompahgre Outfitters, Inc.
Chris Hutchison
USAF Academy Outdoor
Adventure
Mike Bosso
Ute Trail Guide Service
Glenn Everett
Vail Fishing Guides
Mark C. Lokay
Vail Rod & Gun Club
Michael James Jouflas
Valhalla-Bijou, Inc.
Valley Hunting Service
Cliff Bankston
Valley View Ranch
James Peterson
Vickers Enterprises, Inc
Larry Vickers
Vision Quest - Guided Hunts
Chris Furia
Vista Verde Guest Ranch
John S. Munn
W 3 Outfitters
Dale R. Hopwood
W3 Outfitters
Dale & Sheri Hopwood
Wallace Guides & Outfitters
Bill & Fred Wallace
Walz Guide Service
Jimmie Walz Sr.
Wanderin' Star Charters, Inc.
Gary & Kayron McCoy
Wapiti Company
Mark Malesic
Wapiti Outfitter & Guides, Inc.

Jon Garfall
Wapitti Valley Guide &
Outfitting
Jonathan D. Baysinger
Wardell's Guide Service
Layne Wardell
Wason Ranch
Waterfall Ranch Outfitter
Edwin A Zink
Watkins San Juan Outfitting
Thomas F. Watkins
Watson Ranches
James Lee Watson
Waunita Hot Springs Ranch
Ryan Pringle
Weimer Hunting Camp
Jody C. Weimer
Welder Outfitting Service
Brian & Shawn Welder
Wellsweep Ranches
David R. Seely
West Elk Outfitters
John Hatlem
West Fork Outfitters
G. Eugene Story
Western Colorado Outfitters
Gordon Blay
Western Horizon's Guides &
Outfitters
Myron Morrow
Western Sports
Robert O. Woods
Western States Ranches
Western Waters
Edward J. Lawn
Western Ways Ltd.
Eric Glade
Western Wilderness Outdoor
Adv.
Judy Kay Stewart
Western Wildlife Adventure
Western Wildlife Inc.
Rob Raley
Wetherill Ranch
George Hughes
Whistling Acres Guest Ranch
Bill & Bev Madison
Whistling Elk Outfitters, Inc.
John C. Ziegman
White Pine Ranch
Dennis & Cindy Hall
White River Ranch
David J. Prather
White River Resort
Jack Harrison
Whitewater Rafting
Ken Larson
**Whitewater Voyageurs**
**John Sells**
Wild Country Outfitters
Lloyd & Michael R. Madden
Clinton L
Wild West Outfitters
Allen Kennon
Wildass Outfitters
Robert W. Henry & Chester W.
Mayer
Wilderness Adventures Inc.
Larry Ehardt
Wilderness Aware Rafting
Joe Greiner
Wilderness Trails Ranch
Gene Roberts
Wilderness West
Gordon Kent & Scott Garber
Williams Guide Service
Patrick C. Williams
Williams Peak Ranch Co.
Michael Miniat
Willow Creek Outfitters
Don Hawkins
Wilton Earle & Sons
Leon Earle

Winding Stair Mountain
Outfitters
Sam Smith
Winterhawk Outfitter, Inc.
Larry L. Amos
Winterhawk Outfitters
Wit's End Guest Ranch &
Resort
im & Lynn Custer
Wolf Creek Outfitters, LLC
Jason Ward
Woodland Ranch
Elaine & Harry Michael Wood
Woodstock Guide & Outfitting
Jack Sours
Yampa River Outfitters
Randall W. Baird
Yampa Valley Outfitters LLC
Mack & Boyd Tallent
Younger Brothers Guiding &
Outfitting
Glen Younger

# IDAHO

Gary Lindstrom
Todd Molitor
David E. Williams
Bruce A. & Donna Edwards
Chris Paul Loomis
Dale R. Robson
Herman C. Kuykendall
Dusty Youren
Tom L. Jarvis
Laren M. Piquet
Michael Wm. Melville
John Hardin
4 x 4 Outfitters, Inc
Gary Madsen
62 Ridge Outfitters
Ken & Elizabeth Smith
A-W Wilderness Outfitters
Sandy Podsaid
Action Hunts
Charles Loeschen
Aggipah River Trips
Bill Bernt
Aggipah River Trips
Alaska Skagway Outfitters
Chadd Harbaugh
Allison Ranch, Inc.
Harold Thomas
American Adrenaline
Company, Inc.
Deb Wood & Steven E. Zettel
Anderson Creek Outfitters
Edmondson & Nanette M.
Klingback
Anderson Outfitting
Robert and Mary Anderson
Antelope Valley Outfitters, Inc.
Harold E. Smith, Jr.
Arta River Trips
Artic Creek Lodge
Jack P. Smith
B-Bar-C Outfitters
Michael J. Stockton
B & K Outfitters
Brian E. Butz
B Bar C Outfitters
Mike & Belinda Stockton
Barker-Ewing River Trips
Barker River Trips, Inc.
John A. K. Barker
Barker Trophy Hunts
Jon Barker
Bass Fishing with Darl
Darl Ray Hagey
Beamer's Landing
F. James & Jill Koch
Beamer's Landing/Hells

Canyon Tours
Jim & Jill Koch
Bear Creek Outfitters
Lyle Phelps
Bear River Outfitters
Marriner R. Jensen
Bear Valley River Co
Elisabeth A. Boren
Big Track Outfitters
Johannsen & Johannsen
Bigfoot Outfitters
Harvey Whitten & Tom Fliss
Bighorn Outfitters
George Butcher & Dave Melton
Birch Creek & Clearwater
Driftr.
David L. Peterson
Blue Ribbon Charters
Richard D. Lindsey
Bolinder's Country Store
Terry Bolinder
Boren Outdoor Adventures, Inc.
Elisabeth Boren
Boulder Creek Outfitters Inc.
Tim Craig & Allen D. Jones
Bressler Outfitters
Gary Beebe
Bristol Bay Sportfishing, Inc.
Bruce Johnson
BS Flies & Tackle
Bill Schiess
Bugling Bull Archery Outfitters
Rocky Jacobsen
C & M Adventures
Ron Bloxham
C & M Adventures
James Miller
C & M Adventures
Ryan Miller
C & M Adventures
Tim Crist
C Bar D Outfitters
Darrell Meddle
Canyons Incorporated
Leslie W. Bechdel
Caribou Bird Preserve
Cascade Adventures
Jeff S. Hennessy
Cascade Raft & Kayak
Tom Long
Castaway Fly Shop
Daniel Lee Roope
**Castle Creek Outfitters & Guest Ranch**
**Shane & Gwenn McAfee**
Cat Track Outfitters
Todd Molitor
Cayuse Outfitters
Patti & Rich Armiger & Steve Ayers
Cee-Bar-Dee Outfitters
Darrell Weddle
Central Idaho Outfitters
Stephen A. Kaschmitter
Chamberlain Basin Outfitters, Inc.
Tony & Tracy Krekeler
Chuckar Chasers
Rick Schultsmeier
Clayne Baker's Stonefly Anglers
Clearwater Outfitters
Thomas J. Rucker
Clearwater Outfitters
Clearwater River Company
James A. Cook
Clifford Cummings Outfitter
Clifford O. Cummings, Jr.
Coeur d'Alene Outfitters
Murray D. "Bat" Masterson
Coeur D'Alene River Big Game Outfitters

Gary & Jan Sylte
Cook's Idaho & Wind River Outfitters
Rick & Judy Cook
Cougar Country Lodge
Jason M. Schultz
Cross Outfitters
Larry W. Cross
Diamond Charters
Edwin A. Dickson
Diamond D Ranch - Idaho
Diamond D Ranch Inc.
Thomas & Linda Demorest
Diamond D Ranch, Inc.
Thomas & Linda Demorest
Discovery River Expeditions, Inc.
Lester Lowe
Dixie Outfitters, Inc.
Ron & Brad West Pat
Don's Float Tubing Adventures
Don Lehmen
Drifters Landing
John McClatchy
Drifters of the South Fork
Drury Family
Omer Drury
E & Z Inc./Whitewater Outfitters
Zeke & Erlene West
Eakin Ridge Outfitters
Lesley & Lamont Anderson
Elkhorn Village Stables
Daniel P. Mulick
Epley's Whitewater Adventures
Ted Epley
Excel Adventures
Scott Childs
Exodus Corporation
Jr. & Tony Bradbury Richard A. Bradbury
Fall Creek Outfitters
Dalbert (Del) Allmon
Far & Away Adventures
Steve Lentz
Fish Creek Lodging
Janet Keefer
Flying B Ranch, Inc.
Robert Burlingame & Donald Wilson
Flying Resort Ranches Inc.
William R Guth & David E Williams
Full Spectrum Tours
George E. Duncan Outfitter
George E. Duncan
Gillihan's Guide Service
Robert J. Gillihan
Gilmore Ranch Outfitters & Guides
Charles D. Neill, Jr.
Gospel Mountain Outfitters
Jim Daude
**Granite Creek Guest Ranch**
**Carl & Nessie Zitlau**
Granite Creek Ranch
Carl Zitlau
Guth's Iliamna River Lodge
Norman Guth
Guth (Norman H) Inc.
Norman H Guth & Mel Reingold
Hagerman Valley Outfitters, Inc.
Bret C. Silver
Happy Hollow Vacations
Martin Capps
Hat Point Outfitters
Marlin & Susan Kennedy
**Headwaters River Company**
**Betsy Bader**
Conrad Fourney

Heart Mountain Outfitters
Timothy N. Thomas
Heinrich & Smith Outfitters
William Heinrich & Robert Smith
**Heise Expeditions**
Heise Hot Springs, Inc.
Robert M. Quinn
Hell's Canyon Lodge
Reed J. Taylor
Hells Canyon Fishing Charters
Cook & Spickelmire
Henry's Fork Anglers
Mike Lawson
Henry's Fork Anglers, Inc.
Michael J. Lawson
Hidden Creek Ranch
Iris & John Behr
High Adventure Air Charter
Monte Mason
High Adventure River Tours, Inc.
Randy McBride
High Country Outfitters
Ray Seal
High Desert Enterprises
Andrede & Chris Maisel
High Desert Expeditions
Rodger Tiffany
High Desert Ranch, Inc.
Jay Reedy & Jeffrey Widener
High Llama Wilderness Tours, Inc.
Cutler Umbach
High Roller Excursions
Lee Edding
Hincks Palisades Creek Ranch
Bret Hincks
Holiday River Expeditions of Idaho
Harold (Frogg) Stewart
**Horse Creek Outfitters, Inc.**
**Jim Thomas & Rick Trusnovec**
Huckleberry Heaven Lodge
Hughes River Expeditions, Inc.
Jerry Hughes
Hyde Outfitters
Idaho Adventure River Trips
**Idaho Afloat**
**Bruce Howard**
Idaho Angling Service
David T. Glasscock
Idaho Fishing Charters
William J. Spicklemire
Idaho Guide Service, Inc.
James L. Powell
Idaho Whitetail Guides
Jack M. Skille
Idaho Whitewater Unlimited
Shelly Fisher
Indian Creek Guest Ranch
Jon Bower
Indian Creek Ranch Inc.
Jack W. Briggs
Inland Charter Service
Cal Butterfield
Intermountain Excursions
Darell Bentz
J & J Oufitters
James E. Champion
Jacobs Island Park Ranch
F. Mitch Jacobs
Jarbidge Wilderness Guide & Packing
Lowell & Diane Prunty
Joe Cantrell Outfitting
Joe Cantrell
Juniper Mountain Outfitters, Inc.
Stanley & Paul Meholchick
Keating Outfitters
Earl R. Keating, Jr.
Kingfisher Expeditions

Steve F. Settles
Klessig's Guide Service
Jeffrey Klessig
Kuykendall Outfitters, Inc.
Leroy M. Kuykendall
L-B Fishing & Guide Service
Ronald W. Bloxham
L & D Fly Fishing/Three Rivers Ranch
Lonnie Lee Allen
Robert A. Carbone
Last Chance Outfitters, Inc.
Lynn Sessions
Lazy J Outfitters, Inc.
Larry A. Jarrett
Lemburg's Priest Lake Outfitters
Randall Lemburg
Little Wood River Outfitters
Robert L. Hennefer
Lochsa River Outfitters
Sherry & Jacey Nygaard
Lochsa River Outfitters
Jacey Nygaard
Loon Creek Ranch Inc.
Lyle M. Thomas
Lost Lakes Outfitters Inc.
Albert & Diane Latch
Lost River Outfitters
Scott G. Schnebly
Mackay Bar Corporation
Vince Ivanoff
Mackay Wilderness River Trips, Inc.
Brent Estep
Mainstream Outdoor Adventures, Inc.
Charles Alan Lamm
Middle Fork Lodge, Inc.
Mary Ossenkop & Scott Farr
Middle Fork Rapid Transit #1
Greg Edson
Middle Fork River Tours
Kurt Selisch
Middle Fork River Tours, Inc.
Phil B. Crabtree
Middle Fork Wilderness Outfitters, Inc.
Gary Shelton
Middlefork Ranch Inc.
Jimm Sullivan & Bill Widgren
Mile Hi Outfitters Inc.
Jerry Jeppson & Cliff Zielke
Moose Creek Outfitters
Darrell Norris
Moose Creek Ranch, Inc.
Kelly Van Orden
Moser's Idaho Adventures
Gary L. Moser
Moyie River Outfitters
Stanley A. Sweet
Mystic Saddle Ranch
Jeff & Deb Bitton
Mystic Saddle Ranch
Jeff & Deb Bitton
N ID Border Ranch Oftr. & Guide Serv.
Ardella E. Book
National Outdoor Leadership School
Benjamin R. Hammond
Norman H. Guth, Inc.
Norman Guth & Mel Reingold
North Fork Guides
Kenneth R. Hill
North Fork Store & Cafe
North Star Outfitters
Kenneth Wolfinbarger & Les Udy
Northwest River Company
Douglas A. Tims
**Northwest Voyageurs**

Jeff W. Peavey
Oars + Dories, Inc.
Curtis M. Chang
Ospry Adv./Meadow Creek Outfitters
Cheryl Bransford
Ospry Adventures
Cheryl Bransford
Oswold Pack Camp
Ralph Oswold
Oswold Pack Camp
Ralph Oswold
Pack Bridge Outfitters
Robert Hamilton
Pend Oreille Charters Ltd. Co.
Dan Jacobson & Keith Snyder
Pioneer Mountain Outfitters
Tom & Deb Proctor
Pippin Plantation
Priest Lake Guide Service
Gary Brookshire
Priest Lake Outdoor Adventures
Pat Prentice
Quarter Circle A Outfitters
Rick Hussey
R&R Outdoors, Inc.
Robert D. Black
R.O.W. /River Odysseys West
Peter Grubb & Betsy Bowen
Rapid River Outfitters
Kerry Neal Brennan
Rawhide Outfitters
Kathy John Cranney
Red River Corrals
Archie H. George
Red River Outfitters
Lawrence W. Smith
Red Woods Outfitters
Nolan F. Woods
Redfish Lake Lodge
Jack See
Reel Women Fly Fishing Adv.
Renshaw Outfitting, Inc.
Jim & Lynda Renshaw
Rider Ranch
Ridge Runner Outfitters
Ray Christopherson
River "1" Inc.
Dannie A. Strand
River Adventures, Ltd.
Sam Whitten
River Mountain Wildlife Experiences
Shannon Lindsey
River Odyssey's West, Inc.
Peter H. Grubb
River Quest Excursions
Alan W. Odegaard
Robson Outfitters
Dale R. & Janette Robson
Rocky Mountain River Tours, Inc.- David F. Mills
Rudeen Ranches
Kent A. Rudeen
S & S Outfitters
David J. Bream
Saddle Springs Trophy Outfitters
Bruce Cole
Salmon River Challenge, Inc.
Patrick L. Marek
Salmon River Experience
Charles C. & Linda Boyd
Salmon River Lodge Inc.
Jim Dartt
Salmon River Outfitters
Steven W. Shephard
Salmon River Tours Co.
Michael D. McLain
Salmon Valley Guide Service
Kathleen Rae Gliksman
Sawtooth Guide Service, Inc.

Robert L. Cole
Sawtooth Mountain Guides
Kirk D. Bachman
Sawtooth Rentals Inc.
Sawtooth Wilderness Outfitters
Darl & Kari Allred
Scenic River Charters
Timothy L. Jewett
Seagull Charters
James H. Meneely
See Fish Ventures, Inc.
Tom Ellefson
Selway Lodge, Inc.
Rick Hussey & Patricia G. Millington
Sentinel Rock Outfitters
Ray Kagel
Seven Devils Ranch
Rich & Judy Cook
Sevy Guide Service, Inc.
Robert J. Sevy
Shattuck Creek Ranch & Outfitters
Andre Molsee
Shepp Ranch Idaho
Jinny Hopfenbeck & Paul Resnick
Shepp Ranch Idaho
Virginia Hopfenbeck
Silver Cloud Expeditions, Inc.
Jerry Myers
Silver Creek Outfitters, Inc.
Terry W. Ring & Roger Schwartz
Silver Spur Outfitter
Lynn Dalton Tomlison
Skyline Hunting Club & Clays
Sleeping Deer Outfitters Inc.
Ronald J. Clark
Small Cattle Company
Butch Small
Smith River Outfitters, Inc.
Gary D. Lindstrom
Smoky Mountain Outfitters
Bruce T. Butler
Smoky Mountain Outfitters
Bruce T. Butler
Snake River Adventures
Michael L. Luther
Snake River Outfitters
Norman E. Riddle
Snake River Pack Goats
Steven A. Silva
Snug Outfitters, Inc./B. Mason Outfitters
William W. Mason, Jr.
Solitude River Expeditions
South Ford Expeditions, Ltd.
John Hill, Jr.
South Fork Lodge
Spence Warner
South Fork Outfitters
Ralph L. Hatter
Southern Latitudes Fly Fishing — Chile
St. Joe Hunting & Fishing Camp, Inc.
Will & Barbara Judge
Stanley Potts Outfitters
Stan & Joy Potts
Steel Mountain Outfitters
Ronald L. Sherer
Sulphur Creek Ranch
Tom T. Allegrezza
Sun Valley Outfitters, Inc.
Todd Van Bramer
Sun Valley Rivers Company, Inc.
Jon Charles McGregor
Swiftwater Steelhead Trips
Roger J. Monger
Taylor Ranch Outfitters

Steve Zettel
Teton Ridge Guest Ranch
Albert Tilt, III
Teton Valley Lodge, Inc.
Randy Berry
Tews Ranches
The Last Resort
Jimmie Dwayne Blair
The Lodge at Palisades Creek
Chip Kearns
The River Company
Olivia Falconer James
Thousand Springs Tours
J. Russell LeMoyne
Three Rivers Outfitters
James B. Maxwell
Three Rivers Resort & Campground
George Michael & Marie Smith
Tite Line Fishing
John Seidel
Towle Outfitters
Gary R. Towle
Trail Creek Outfitters, Inc.
Layne Davis
Triangle C Ranch's
Ron Gillett
Triple O Outfitters, Inc.
D.A. & Barbara Opdahl Harlan
Trophy Trout Outfitters & Guides Service
Richard R. Reinwald
Trout Creek Outfitters, Inc.
Ray & BarBetta Cox
Twin Peaks Ranch Inc.
Dave Giles
Two M River Outfitters, Inc.
Michael W. Murphy
Victor Frederickson Outfitter & Guide
Victor Frederickson
WSRT Birds of Prey Expeditions
Wally York & Son, Inc.
W. Travis York
Wapiti Meadow Ranch & Outfitters
M. Barry Bryant & Diane Haynes
Wapiti River Guides
Gary Lane
War Eagle Outfitters & Guides
Ken & Dolly Jafek
Warm Springs Outfitters
Gordon E. Frost
Warren River Expeditions, Inc. - David F. Warren
Watermark Adventures
Pat Harper
Weitas Creek Outfitters
Steve F. Jones
Western Frontier Adventures
Richard A. Hankins
Western Pleasure Guest Ranch
Whiskey Mountain Outfitters
James I. Bass
White Cloud Outfitters
Mike Scott & Louise Stark
White Otter Outdoor Adventures
Randy P. Hess
White Outfitters
Bill G. White
White Water West
Gail Watt
White Water West
Stan Watt
Whitewater Adventures Idaho
Kenneth C. Masoner
Whitewater Outfitters
Zeke & Erlene West
Whitewater Shop River Tours
Stephen J. Guinn

Whitewater Wilderness Lodge
Wild Horse Creek Ranch
William R. Shields & Claire Casey
Wild Idaho Outfitters, Inc.
Frank Giles
Wilderness Outfitters
Podsaid & Hart
Wilderness Outfitters
Shelda, Justin & Jarrod Farr
Scott
Wilderness River Outfitters & Trail Exp.
Joseph Lewis Tonsmeire
Willey Ranch Outfitters/ B & B
Davis
Buzz Davis
Worldwide Outdoor Adventures
Randy Beck
Yellow Wolf Ranch
Edd S. Woslum

## MONTATA

David M. Krogedal
James & Pattie Slack
Dennis G. Kavanagh
William L Davis
Gerald R. Clark
Daniel E. Glines
Allan W. Gadoury
Justin Johns
Scott G. Hibbard
Richard Johnson
Tony E. Jorgenson
Bill Burwell
Ross Childers
James K. Tyler
Doug Swisher
William L. Davis
Todd Andrew Wester
Dudley L. Tyler
Bill Ternes
LeRoy G. Senter
Paul Updike
Lee Kinsey
Jennifer Olsson
Kurt J. Olson
Robert E. Flynn
Eric T. Swedman
Glenna Stevenson
Cherster L. Marion
David J. Lueck
Bill Hooker
Beyond All Roads Klicks K Bar L
Wild Eyes Wildlife Adventures
10,000 Waves, Raft & Kayak Adventures
Deb Moravec
320 Ranch
5/S Outfitting & Guide Service
Glenn E. Smith
63 Ranch
Sandra M. Cahill
7 Lazy P Ranch
7C Quarter Circle Outfitters
Dennis P. Chatlain
7W Guest Ranch
Glenda S. Reynolds
9 Quarter Circle Ranch
Kim Kelsey
9T9 Ranch
A-1 Fishing
Craig Renfro
A-Able Fishing Charters
George Goggins
A Lazy H Outfitters
Allen J. Haas
A Lazy H Outfitters
Allen J. Haas

Absaroka Outfitters
Vernon T. Smith
Absaroka Rafting Adventures
Absaroka River Adventures
Matt Holtz
Adventure Motorsports
Larry Eddy
Adventure Whitewater
Marek Rosin
Adventures
Adventures Big Sky
Patrick Dillon
Al Bassett Montana Outfitter
Al Bassett
Al Gadoury's 6X Outfitters
Allan W. Gadoury
Al Troth Fly Fishing Guide
Service
Alfred C. Troth
Al Wind's Trout Futures
Alan Wind
Alaska Flyfishing Expeditions
Thomas & Virginia Leroy
Allaman's Montana Adventure
Kenneth C. Allaman
Aller's Boulder River Ranch
Steve & Jeane Aller
Alta Meadow Ranch
Britt Litchford
American Hunting Services
Guy Shanks
American Hunting Services
Anchor Outfitting
Charles M. Rein
Anderson's Yellowstone Angler
George R. Anderson
Angler's Edge
Paul R. Rice
Anglers Afloat, Inc.
David J. O'Dell
Antelope Creek Outfitters
Paul Cornwell
Antlers Guide Service
George H. Athas
Anvil Butte Ranch
Arctic Tern Charter
William Grasser
Arrick's Fishing Flies
Arrick Lyle Swanson
At the Summit Outfitting
Service
Atcheson Outfitting
John D. "Jack" Atcheson
Autumn Brown Outfitting
Alvin Blakley
Avalanche Basin Outfitters
Douglas Caltrider
Avalanche Basin Outfitters
Douglas Caltrider
Averill's Flathead Lake Lodge
Doug & Maureen Averill
Avon Outfitters
Robert D. Cunningham
B & D Outfitters
Robert D. FrisK
B Bar Two Outfitters
Lance C. Vines
Babcock Creek Outfitters
LeRoy Books
Babcock Creek Outfitters
Leroy E. Books
Back Country Outfitter &
Charter
Elbert Loomis
Bad Beaver Bikes, Skis & Tours
Susan Renfro
Badland Buck & Bull Outfitters
Lee A. Zeller
Bales Hunts
Keith Bales
Bales Hunts
Keith Bales
Bar N Ranch

Wayne Trukowski
Bar Six Outfitters
Terry D. Throckmorton
Bar Y Seven Ranch
Claude Saylor
Barlett Creek Outfitters
Mike Smith
Barnes Brothers, Inc.
Jack R. Joyce
Bartlett Creek Outfitters
Mike Smith
Battle Creek Lodge
Battle Creek Outfitters
Larry Richtmyer
Bear's Den Outfitters, Inc.
Bruce C. Delorey
Bear Creek Guest Ranch
William Beck
Bear Creek Lodge
Roland & Elizabeth Turney
Bear Creek Outfitters & Guest
Ranch
Bill Beck
Bear Creek Ranch & Outfitters
William E. Beck
Bear Paw Mountain Outfitters
Eric M. Olson
Bear Paw Outfitters
Tim Bowers
Bear Trap Outfitters
Kenneth R. Whitman
Beardsley Outfitting & Guide
Service
Tim Beardsley
Beartooth Flyfishing
Daniel J. Delekta
Beartooth Plateau Outfitters
Ronnie L. Wright
Beartooth Plateau Outfitters
Ronnie L. Wright
Beartooth Ranch & JLX
Outfitters
James E. Langston
Beartooth Whitewater
Randow Parker
Beartrap Express
Johnny C. France
Beaver Creek Outfitters
Clayton A. Barkhoff
Beaverhead Anglers
Paul George Wiedeman
Beaverhead/Bighole River
Angle
Shawn Lester Jones
Beavertail Outfitters
Dennis Rehse
Bell Ranch Outfitting
Bill Meeks
Benchmark Wilderness Guest
Ranch
Darwin Heckman
Benchmark Wilderness Ranch
Darwin C. Heckman
Big "M" Outfitters
Robert E. Hogue
Big Bear Lodge
Scott Sanders
Big Bear Lodge, Inc.
Alan R. Harris
Big Cir Outfitters & Lodge
Stanley A. Cirspinski
Big Dipper Charters
Dave Minister
Big Hole River Outfitters
Craig Fellin
Big Horn River Lodge
Phil Gonzales
Big Horn River Outfitters
Gael T. Larr
Big Horn Trout Shop
Steve M. Hilbers
Big Rivers Guide Service
Don Burks

Big Salmon Outfitters
Richard Kehoe Wayman
Big Sky Expeditions
Joel S. Wiemer
Big Sky Expeditions
Big Sky Flies & Guides
Garry McCutcheon
Big Sky Guide & Outfitters
Tom D. Brogan
Big Sky Outfitters
Richard F Kountz
Big Sky Overland Cruises
Big Sky Roping Ranch
Big Sky Sporting Clays
Van Voast Farms
Big Sky Trophy Outfitters
Sam C. Borla
Big Timber Guides
Robert J. Bovee
Bighorn Angler
Mike Craig & Tom McClure
Bighorn Angler
Donald R. Cooper
Bighorn Country Outfitters
George Kelly
Bighorn Country Outfitters
George J. Kelly
Bighorn River Fin & Feathers
James L. Pickens
Bighorn River Lodge
Phil Y. Gonzalez
Bighorn River Shop/Lazy Boot
Outfitters
Bighorn Trout Shop
Hale C. Harris & Steve Hilbers
Bighorn Troutfitters, Inc.
Joseph D. Caton
Bill Johnson Outfitters
Bill Mitchell Outfitters, Inc.
William H. & Karen Mitchell
Billingsley Ranch Outfitters
Jack Billingsley
Birch Creek Outfitters
William W. Galt
Birch Creek Outfitters
Laddie Peverley
Birch Creek Outfitters
Rick Peverley
Birds of Plenty
Bitterroot Anglers
Andre August Carlson
Bitterroot Outfitters
Thomas L. & Shannon
Henderson
Black Butte Outfitters
J.O. Hash, Jr.
Black Mountain Outfitters
Glen Scott Sallee
Black Otter Guide Service
Duane Neal
Blackbird's Fly Shop & Lodge
Blacktail Ranch
Sandra Renner
Blizzard Mountain Outfitters
Nicholas Smetana
Blue Nugget Outfitters
Eugene R. Knight
Blue Quill Fly Co.
Robert E. Krumm
Blue Ribbon Fishing Tours
Dale D. Siegle
Blue Ribbon Flies
Craig R. Mathews
Blue Ribbon Guide Service
Anthony A. Schoonen
Blue Ridge Outfitters
Earl Ray Shores
Blue Rock Outfitters
O. Kurt Hughes
Blue Spruce Lodge & Guest
Ranch
Bob's Tackle Box
Bob A. Cleverley

Bob Jacklin's Fly Shop, Inc.
Bob Jacklin
Bob Marshall Wilderness
Ranch
Virgil B. Burns
Bob Marshall Wilderness
Ranch
Bonanza Creek Country
Borderline Outfitters
Miles Hutton
Boulder River Fly Fishing
Company
Brad Downey's Angler's Edge
Brad Downey
Brant Oswald Fly Fishing
Service
Brant Konrad Oswald
Bridger Mountain Guide
Service
James R. Brogan
Bridger Outfitters
David B. Warwood
**Broken Arrow Lodge**
**Erwin & Sherry Clark**
Broken Hart Ranch
Lee I. Hart
Broken Heart Guest Ranch
Bernard C. Nieslanik
Broken Horn Outfitters
Ken D. Murdoch
Broken V Guest Ranch
Buck Creek Ranch Guide
Service
Thomas W. Parker
**Buckhorn Ranch Outfitters**
**Harry T. Workman**
Bud Lilly's Trout Shop
Dick Greene
Buffalo Creek Outfitters
John & DruAnn Robidou
Buffalo Creek Ranch
Dixie Myhre
Buffalo Jump Outfitting, LLC
Bugle Ridge Outfitters
John A. Keenan
Bull Lake Guest Ranch
Bull Mountain Outfitters
M.J. "Mike" Murphy
Bull Mountain Outfitters
M.J. Murphy
Bull Mountain Outfitters
Bull Mtn. Outfitters
M. Murphy
Bull River Outfitters
Doug Peterson
Bull Run Outfitters
Bud Heckman
Bull Run Outfitters & Guest
Ranch
Joe Tripp
Bullseye Outfitting
Jeff Smith
Bunky Ranch Outfitters
DeVon "Smut" Warren
Burke Ranch
Don J. Burke
Burns Creek Outfitters
Alan R. Klempel
C-B Ranch
Sandy VanderLans
C-Bar Heart Guest Ranch &
Lodge
Cabin Creek Outfitters
Kenneth W. Phillips
Cabinet Divide Outfitters
Terry N. Kayser
Cabinet Mountain Adventures,
Inc.
Bill & Ken
Cabinet Mountain Outfitters
Gerald & Vikki Carr
Cameron Outfitters
Del Cameron

Camp Baker Outfitters
Donald W. Johnson
Camp Creek Inn B & B Guest Ranch
Canoeing House/Blue Ribbon Guide
Allan L. Anderson
Canyon & Creek Outfitters
Lyle S. Bainbridge
Canyon Creek Guest Ranch
David L. Duncan
Canyon Creek Ranch
Captain Trout Outfitter & Guides
Robert Coppock
Careless Creek Getaway
Cargill Outfitting
John C. Cargill
Cast and Blast Outfitters
Curt D. Collins
Castle Creek Outfitters & Guest Ranch
John D. Graham
Castle Lodge
D. Castle Smith
Castle Mountain Fly Fishers
Dillon S. Dempsey
Cat Track Outfitters
Cal Thornberg
Catch Montana
John N. Adza
Cayuse Outfitters
Larry A. Lahren
CB Cattle & Guest Ranch
Cedar Breaks Outfitters
John A. Stuver
Centennial Guest Ranch
Centennial Outfitters
Mel W. Montgomery
Central Montana Outfitters
Chad S. Schearer
Centre Island Resort
David Ballinger & Laura St. John
Chan Welin's Big Timber Fly Fishing
Channing W. Welin
**Chase Hill Outfitters**
**William L. Brown**
**Cheff's Guest Ranch**
Mick & Karen Cheff
Chico Hot Springs Lodge
Colin Davis
Chris Branger, Outfitter
Chris W. Branger
Cinnamon Lodge
Marc Newcomb
Circle Bar Guest Ranch
Sarah Stevenson
Circle KBL Outfitters & Guides
Robert A. Lamberson
Clark's Guide Service
Edward C. Clark
Clearwater Outfitters
Tom Ziberman
Clearwater Outfitters
Larry J. Kenney
Climbing Arrow Outfitters
F. & M. Anderson
Coman's Guide Service
Stan Coman
Combs Outfitting
Tim T. Combs
Continental Divide Outfitters
Walter D. Easley
Copenhaver Outfitters, Inc.
Steven D. Copenhaver
Copper River Fly Fishing Lodge
Jeff & Pat Vermillion
Cottonwood Outfitters
John A. Wilkinson
Cougar Ranch Outfitters

Buck Wood
Cougar Ridge Outdoors
William Richard Briggs
Covered Wagon Outfitters
Edward L. Hake
Covered Wagon Ranch
Vic Bensen
**Cow Creek Outfitters**
**John R. Fritz**
Cowboy Outfitters
Gib Lloyd
Coyote Outfitters
Donald E. Mawyer
Crain Outfitting & Guide Service
Richard A. Crain
Crane Meadow Lodge
Robert G. Butler
Crane Mountain Guide Service
Fred W. Buchanan
Crazy Mountain Outfitter & Guide
Phillip Ray Keefer
Crazy Mountain Raft
Robert H. Wiltshire
Crow Creek Outfitters & Guides
Michael E. Parsons
Cudney's Guide Service
David L. Cudney
Cudrey Guide Service
Dave Cudrey
Curry Comb Outfitters
William L. Knox
Curtiss Outfitters
Ronald L. Curtiss
Custom Adventures
Roger Bowers
Custom River Outfitters
J. Ellery & T. Petrick Steven Heaverlo
Dan Bailey's Fly Shop
John P. Bailey
Dave Willborn Outfitter
Dave Willborn
Davis Creek Camp, Inc.
John Luther & greg Pattison
Daystar Guest Ranch
DC Outfitting
Richard L. Cox
Dead Rock Guest Ranch
Sonja Myrstol
Diamond Hitch Outfitters
Chris & Robert McNeill
Diamond J Guest Ranch
Tim Combs
Diamond K Outfitters
Charles D. Kendall
Diamond N Outfitters
Brian D. Nelson
Diamond R Guest Ranch
James A. Slack
Diamond R. Expeditions
Peter Rothing
Dick Lyman Outfitters
Dick P. Lyman
DL Elk Outfitters, Inc.
Dennis A. LeVeque
DN & 3 Outfitters
Eldon H. Snyder
Don Carvey Outfitting
Donald R. Carvey
Donohoe Outfitting
Paul T. Donohoe
Doonan Gulch Outfitters
Russell E. Greenwood
Double Arrow Outfitters/Rich Ranch
Jack C. Rich
Double R Outfitting & Guide Service
Glen Nepil
Double Shot Doc Ranch

**Double Spear Ranch**
**Tony Blackmore**
Douglas Fir & Furs
Douglas H. Gauf
Douglas Roberts Outfitter
Douglas A. Roberts
DRGA Ranch
Mr. & Mrs. Drga
Eagle Creek Outfitters
Charles Tuchschmidt
**Eagle Nest Lodge**
**Keith Kelly**
Eagle Nest Lodge/Lazy Boot Outfitters
Nick C. Forrester
East Boulder River Guest House
East Fork Outfitters
Mark McKee
East Fork Outfitters
Mark A. McKee
**East Slope Anglers/Mad Wolf Ski - Brad R. Parsch**
East Slope Outfitters
James R. Laughery
Eastslope Outfitters
Anthony John Fowler
ECOLLAMA
David Harmon
Ed Curnow Outfitters
Edward E. Curnow
Elk Creek Outfitters
Gerald K. Olson
Elk Creek Outfitters
Thomas J. Francis
**Elk Creek Outfitting**
**Brent & Kathy Fitchett**
Elk Range Outfitters
William J. Montanye
Elk Ridge Outfitters
Doug & Michelle Landers
Elkhorn Enterprises
Pete Clark
Elkhorn Outfitters
Henry T. Barron
Elkhorn Outfitters, Inc.
Henry T. Barron
Elkhorn Ranch
Linda Miller
**Esper's Under Wild Skies Lodge & Outfitters**
**Vaughn Esper**
Espresso Outfitters
Espy Ranch
Jim Espy
**EW Watson & Sons Outfitting**
**Ed & Wanda Watson**
Experience Montana
Allen Schallenberger
F & M Ranch Outfitters
Floyd Price
Faber Ranch
Leo M. Faber
Fallon Creek Outfitters
Monte Berzel
Firehole Ranch
Fischer's Fishers
Dennis C. Fischer
Fish Montana
Leonard Moffo
Fishing Head Quarters
Brete Thibeault
Fishing Headquarters
Dick Sharon
Five Bears Outfitters
Gary Peters
Five Valleys Flyfishers
Chris E. Nelson
**Flat Iron Outfitting**
**Jerry C. Shively**
Flathead Trophy Fly Fishers
George D. Widener
Flatline Outfitters

Matthew Greemore
Flowing Rivers Guide Service
D.L. Tennant
Fly-Fishing Montana Company
Randall J. Ziegler
Fly Fishers' Inn
Richard W. Pasquale
Fly Fishing Unlimited
Donald R. Lyman
Flyfishing Adventures
L. Darryl Osburn
Flyfishing Montana & Chile
Michael C. Mosolf
Flying D Ranch
Rob Arnaud
Flying Diamond Guide Service
Jack W.P. Davis
Flying Eagle Ranch
Wayne H. Mackie
Flying S Outfitting
Duane L. Nollmeyer
Flying W Outfitters
Sherry Ann Ward
Ford Creek Outfitters
Elizabeth Barker
Fork Peck Outfitting, Inc.
Jane Waldie
Four Rivers Fishing Co.
Four Six Outfitters
Fred Ennist
Fowler's Charter & Rental
Harry D. Fowler
Frontier Anglers
Timothy M. Tollett
Ft. Musselshell Outfitters
Bill Harris
G Bar M Ranch
Burl & LaNelle Kirkland
Gallatin Riverguides
Steven French
Gary Evans Madison River Guides
Gary Webb Guide & Outfitters
Gary Webb
George Klemens Outfitting
George C. Klemens
Geyser Whitewater Expeditions, Inc.
Eric Becker
Glacier Fishing Charters
James P. Landwehr
Glacier Outfitters
Gary Abbey
Glacier Raft Co.
Sally Thompson
Glacier Raft Co.
Daniel Howlett
Glacier Raft Co.
Onno C. Wieringa
Glacier Sea Kayaking
Bobbie Gilmore
Glacier Wilderness Guides
Cris Gayner
Glacier Wilderness Guides, Inc.
Randy M. Gayner
Golden Bear Outfitters
Walter C. Earl
Golden Sedge Drifters
Gregory A. Childress
Gone Clear Outfitters
Dave Hall
**Good's Bird Hunts/Eagle Outfitters - Gerry W. Good**
Great Basin Hunters
Gerald Nyman
Great Bear & Landers Fork Outfitters
H.J. Gilchrist
Great Bear Outfitters
H.J. Gilchrist
Great Divide Guiding/Outfitters

Richard T. Jackson
Great Divide Outfitters
Albert F. Lefor
Great Northern Fishing
Great Northern Llama Co., Inc.
Steve C. Rolfing
Great Northern Outfitters
Ken Mitchell
Great Northern Whitewater
Great Northern Whitewater, Inc.
Deedee Baldwin
Great Waters Outfitters
Mark A. Lane
Great Waters Outfitting
John Keeble
Greater Yellowstone Flyfishers
Greyson Creek Meadows Rec.
Ted Flynn
Grizzly Hackle Outfitters
James Edward Toth
**Grossenbacher Guides**
**Brian Grossenbacher**
Hailstone Ranch Co.
Samuel Langhus
Hanging "J" Ranch
Joyce G. Rehms
Hank Miller Steelhead
Hank Miller
**Hargrave Cattle & Guest**
**Ranch - Ellen White Hargrave**
Harman's Fly Shop
Thomas J. Harman
**Hatch Finders**
**Dean A. Reiner**
Hawkins Outfitters
Steve Hawkins
Hawkridge Outfitters &
Rodblds
Howard Bethel
Hawley Mountain Guest Ranch
Cathy Johnson
Headwaters Guide Service
Robin Cunningham
Healing Waters Fly Fishing
Lodge
Greg & Janet Lilly
Heaven on Earth Ranch
Heinecke Outfitting & Guide
Service
William F. Heinecke
Hell's A Roarin' Outfitters
Warren H. Johnson
Hell Creek Guest Ranch
John E. Trumbo
Hidden Hollow Hidaway
Ranch
Gary Flynn
**Hidden Hollow Hideaway**
**Kelly & Jill Flynn**
High Country Connection
Dave Lindquist
High Country Connection
Larry C. Trimber
High Country Outfitters
Chip Rizzotto
High Country Outfitters Fly
Fishing Lodge
High Plains Drifter
Mike Hillygus
High Plains Outfitters
Mike Bay
High Valley Ranch
Patrick E. McFall
Highland to Island Guide
Servide
James B. McKillip
Hildreth Livestock Ranch
Donna Hildreth
Hill's Professional Outfitters
Edna V. Hill
Hill Country Expeditions
Lois Hill

Hole in the Wall Outfitters
Todd Earp
Homestead Ranch
Edward F. Arnott
Homestead Ranch
Ed F. Arnott
Horse Creek Outfitters
Robert Bruce Malcolm
Horse Prairie Guest Ranch
Mack & Candi Hedges
Horseshoe Guide Service
Ted E. Dinsdale
Howard Outfitters
Dale Patrick Howard
Howard Zehntner Hunting
Howard Zehntner
Hubbard's Yellowstone Lodge
Hubbard's Yellowstone
Outfitter
James L. Hubbard
Hunters Montana
Keith J. Atcheson
I.C.R. Outfitters
Wade Warren Durham
Iron Horse Outfitters
Art Griffith
**Iron Wheel Ranch**
J-L Outfitters
Arthur J. Stevens
J & J Guide Service
Jamie & Juanita Byrne
Jack River Outfitters
Jim Allison
Jacklin's Outfitters
Robert V. Jacklin
Jackson-Snyder Ranch
Jake's Horses, Inc.
Kent "Jake" Grimm
Jennifer Smith Fly Casting
Jennifer L. Smith
Jerry Crabs Fly Fisher
Jerry Crabs
Jerry Malson Outfitting
Jerry R. Malson
Jess Jones Outfitting Service
Jess D. Jones
Jim McBee Outfitter
James L. McBee
JJJ Wilderness Ranch
Max D. Barker
**JM Bar Outfitters**
**Jeffery & Maria Freeman**
Joe Heimer Outfitting
Joseph A. Heimer
John Greene's Fly Fishing
Service
John J. Greene
John Haney Flyfishing Services
John W. Haney
John Hanson MTI, Inc.
John Hanson
John Maki Outfitters
John C. Maki
John Oppelt Flyfishing
Outfitter
John R. Oppelt
John Perry's West Slope Outfit
John R. Perry
Johnson Outfitters
Kathryn M. Johnson
Johnson Outfitters
Kathryn M. Johnson
Josephson Outfitting
Ed & Lisa Josephson
JR Buffalo Creek Outfitters
John W. Robidou
JR Outfitters
Corky & Clarice Hedrick
JR/Buffalo Creek Outfitters
John W. Robidou
Judith River Ranch
Steve Musick
Jumping Rainbow Ranch

K & D Outfitting
Kenneth L. Torgerson
K & N Outfitting
Wade D. Nixon
K Lazy Three Ranch
Mary Faith Hoeffner
KB Outfitters
Gerald L. "Bo" Kezar
Keenan Ranch/Bugle Ridge
Outfitters
Kent "Jake" Grimm
Kent D. Grimm
KG Guides & Outfitters
Ken D. Graber
**Kibler Outfitting**
**Myron & Mary Beth Kibler**
Kincheloe Outfitting
Robert B. Kincheloe
Klick's K Bar L Ranch
Dick & Nancy Klick
Koocanusa Outfitters
E. Neven Zugg
Koocanusa Resort & Outfitters
Kootenai Angler
David Blackburn
Kootenai High Country
Hunting
David Hayward
Kootenai River Outfitters
Gary McCabe
L Diamond E Ranch Outfitters
Dan J. & Retta Ekstrom
L.S. Adventures
Larry M. Surber
Lake Upsata Guest Ranch
LaMarche Creek Outfitting Co.
Russell B. Smith
Lapham Outfitters
Max & Debbie Lapham
Laredo Enterprises
Lass & Ron Mills Outfitters
Lass Dudley
Last Best Place Tours
Graeme R. McDougal
Last Stand Outfitters
August D. Egdorf
Laughing Water Ranch
Ted & Holly Mikita-Finch
Lazy E-L Working Guest Ranch
Derek Kampfe
Lazy Heart Outfitters
Linda M. Budeski
Lazy JR Outfitters
William S. Crismore
Lazy K Bar Ranch
Tack VanCleve
Lazy T4 Outfitters
Spencer G. Trogdon
Lee Watson Outfitters
Lee W. Watson
Lepley Creek Ranch
Matthew Halmes
Lew & Clark Expeditions Corp.
Michael John Geary
Lewis & Clark Trail Adventures
Wayne Fairchild
Limestone Kamp
Ray Hill
Linehan Outfitting Co.
Timothy Linehan
Lion Creek Outfitters
Cecil L Noble
Little Rockies Outfitting
David L. Rummel
Lloyd V. Johnson, Outfitter &
Guide
Lloyd Johnson
Lochsa Lodge Resort
Susie Denton
Lone Mountain Ranch
Robert L. Schaap
Lone Tree Fly Goods
David W. Borjas

**Lone Tree Outfitting & Guide**
**Service**
**Larry A. Pendleton**
Lone Willow Creek Guide
Service
Jim M. Schell
Lone Wolf Guide Service
Mark A. Baumeister
Lonesome Spur Guest Ranch
Loons Echo Resort
Ed Hynes
Lost Coulee Outfitters
Thomas J. Fisher
Lost Creek Outfitters
Don O. Wright
Lost Creek Outfitting
James Leslie Haynie
Lost Fork Ranch
Merritt G. Pride
Lost Spur Working Ranch
Lower Clark Fork River
Outfitters
Donn R. Dale
Lucky Day Outfitter
Ed Skillman
M & E Outfitters
Keith Meckling
M & M Outfitters
Monty D. Hankinson
M Hanging Cross Outfitters &
Guide
Michael "Chip" Gollehon
M.B.K. Outfitters
Michael B. Krueger
M.B.K. Outfitters
Michael B. Krueger
Madion Valley Ranch
Madison River Fishing Co.
Michael D. Pollack
Madison Valley Cabins
Gary F. Evans
Madson River Outfitters
Robert "Dan" Hull
Mandorla Ranch
Many Rivers Outfitting
Daniel Guy Miller
Maountain Trail Outfitters
David Gamble
Mark Young's Hunting
Services
Mark E. Young
McCabe Outfitters
Gary McCabe
McClain Guest House
McCormick's Sunset Guest
Ranch
Mike C. McCormick
McDonough Outfitters
Robert McDonough
McFarland & White Ranch
Gilbert White
McFarland & White Ranch
Gilber "Mac" White
McKenzie's Sportsmans
Retreat on Rock Creek
McNeely Outfitting
Shawn G. McNeely
Medicine Lake Outfitters
Thomas M. Heintz
Medicine Lake Outfitters
Tom Heintz
Miller Barber's Streamline
Anglers
John Herzer
Miller Outfitters
Robert E. Miller
Milller Outfitters
Robert E. Miller
Ming Coulee Outfitters
James M. Gasvoda
Mission Mountain Outfitters
Richard R. Bishop
Missouri Breaks Adventures

246

John E. Vaia
Missouri River Angler
Peter J. Cardinal
Missouri River Canoe Co.
Don Sorenson
Missouri River Expeditions
Timothy G. Plaska
Missouri River Outfitters, Inc.
Larry Cook
Missouri River Trout Shop
Patrick Alan Elam
Missouri Riverside, Inc.
Leonard A. Gidlow
**Mitchell Outfitting**
**Floyd W. Mitchell**
MJ Outfitting Services
Montana's Master Angler Fly
Service
Thomas M. Travis
Montana Adventures in
Angling
James McFadyean
Montana Bird Hunts
Dennis G. Kavanagh
Montana Blue Ribbon
Outfitters Big Sky
Edward G. Renaud
Montana Breaks Outfitting
Donald B. Lynn
Montana Casting Co.
William Joyner
Montana Experience Outfitter
Carl A. Mann
Montana Fly Fishing
Michael W. Mouat
Montana Fly Fishing
Adventures
Patrick J. Bannon
Montana Flycast
Dennis Kavanagh
Montana Flyfishing Co.
Kirk Johnston
Montana Guide Service
Edwin L. Johnson
Montana High Country
Outfitter
Timothy R. Reishus
Montana High Country Tours,
Inc.
Russell D. Kipp
Montana Outdoor Adventures,
Inc.
Randy J. Cain
Montana Outdoor Expeditions
Robert James Griffith
Montana Outfitter
Alfred S. Bassett
Montana Ranchers Hunts
Lester M. Morgan
Montana River Guides
Gregory G. Mentzer
Montana River Outfitters
R. Craig Madsen
Montana River Ranch
Wagner D. Harmon
Montana River Trips
Daniel Groshens
Montana Riverbend Outfitters
Robert J. Zikan, Sr.
Montana Rivers to Ridges
Daniel J. & Joanne Pluth
Montana Safaris
Rocky J. Heckman
Montana Trail Trophy Outfitter
Michael J. Clark
Montana Trout Club
Montana Trout Trappers
Jim Cox
Montana Troutfitters Orvis
Shop
David L. Kumlien
Montana Whitewater
Bill Zell

Montana Wilderness Outfitters
David & Tena Kozub
Monte's Guiding & Mtn.
Outfitters
LaMonte J. Schnur
Montella From Montana
Richard Montella
**Monture Face Outfitters**
**Tom Ide and Valerie Call**
Monture Outfitters
James L. Anderson
Morgan Guest House
Mossy Horn Outfitters
Gordon W. Sampson
Mountain Leisure Trading Co.
Sherman Brown
Mountain Sky Guest Ranch
Shirley Arnesault
Mountain Trail Outfitters
David B. Gamble
Mountain Trails Outfitters
A. Lee Bridges
Muleshoe Outfitters & Guide
Service
Jack Howser
Musselshell Outfitters
Randy D. Higgins
N-Bar Land & Cattle Company
Thomas E. Elliott
Neal Outfitter's
Danielle Neal
Neal Outfitters
Lloyd Neal
New West Outfitters
David B. Moore
Nez Perce Ranch
**Nine Quarter Circle Ranch**
**The Kelseys**
No Cut Throats Outfitting
Craig A. Clevidence
North Alaska Expeditions
Justin Johns
North Star Outfitters
Everett "EB" Morris
North Yellowstone Outfitters
William H. Hoppe
Northern High Plains
Outfitters
Edwin R. Anderson
Northern Lights Outdoor
Center
John Gangemi
Northern Plains Outfitters
Doug Dreeszenn
Northern Rockies Natural
History
Ken Sinay
Northwest Voyageurs
Northwest Waters Outfitters
Old West Angler & Outfitters
Jim Yeager & Ernie Strum
Osprey Expeditions
Otter Creek Outfitters
James W. Wilkins
Outlaw River Runners/Great
Bear
Greg Nelson
Paintbrush Trails, Inc.
Wanda Wilcox
Painted Rock Outfitters
Mike & Debbie Rodgers
Pangaea Expeditions
Karla James
Parade Rest Guest Ranch
Paradise Adventures
Ned S. Chadbourn
Paradise Fishing Excursions
James R. French
Paradise Outfitters
Jim H. Cooper
Paradise Outfitters
Stephen R. Ayers
Paradise Valley

David R. Handl
Parks' Fly Shop
Richard C. Parks
Parson's Outfitting
Jean Parsons
Paul Roos Outfitters
Paul S. Roos
Paul Tunkis Flyfishing Guide
Service
Paul Tunkis
Pelly Lake Wilderness
Outfitters
Dennis LeVeque
Pepperbox Ranch
Perry Hunts & Adventures
Peterson's Fairmont Corral,
Inc.
William H. Peterson
Pig Eye Outfitters
Peter B. Rogers
Pine Butte Guest Ranch
Pine Hills Outfitters
Robert "Mike" Barthelmess
Pine Ridge/Bartlett Creek
Outfitter
Robert M. Labert
Pioneer Outfitter
Charles A. & Cliff Page
PK Outfitters/Missoulian
Angler
Paul W. Koller
Point of Rocks Guest Ranch
Irvin "Max" Chase
Points Unknown
Powder River Outfitters
Kenneth F. Greslin
Quarter Circle E.M. Outfitters
Ernest E. McCollum
Quill Gordon Fly Fishers
Gordon S. Rose
R.J. Cain & Company Outfitters
R.J. Cain
**R.L. Sourbrine Outfit. & Sons**
**Richard L. Sourbrine**
R.W. Outfitters
Robert W. Wetzel
Rach Outfitters/Flathead
Charters
Jeff E. Rach
Rainbow Chasers
Larry Cawlfield
Rainbow Guide Service
Joseph Daniel Biner
Rainbow Outfitters
Jim L. Becker
Ram Mountain Outfitters
Robert L Neal
**Ramshorn Outfitters**
**Audie & Vivianne Anderson**
Randy Brown's Madison
Flyfisher
Randall W. Brown
Randy Petrich Big Game Hunts
Randy Petrich
Randy Rathie Outfitter
Range Riders Ranch
Terry & Wyoma Terland
Rawhide Guide Service
Leroy A. Fatouros
Ray Perkins Outfitter
J. Ray Perkins
Red Mountain Outfitters
Les G. Nader
Redbone Outfitting
Carl "Bud" Martin
Rendezvous Outfitters
Herbert A. Moore
Reynolds Hollowtop Hideaway
Harvey D. Reynolds
**Rich Ranch LLC**
**Rick Wemple Outfitting/**
**Wildlife Adv.**
**Richard J. Wemple**

Rimrock Ridge Outfitters
Roy L. Coneen
River Bend Flyfishing
Charles Miles Stranahan
River Breaks Outfitting
Rick R. Wood
River Quest Angler
Bob Swain
River Resource Enterprises
Mark Jones
River Road Outfitters
Herbert Weiss
Riveride Motel & Outfitters
Robert Hines
RJR Ranch
RL Outfitters
Dwain Rennaker
Robert Butler Outfitting
Robert G. Butler
Robert Dolatta Outfitters
Robert Dolatta
Robert Dupea Outfitters
Robert L. Dupea
Rock Creek Fishing Co.
John Erp
Rock Creek Outfitters
Dean Armbrister
**Rocky Fork Guide Service**
**Ernest C. Strum**
Rocky Mountain Adventures
Daniel J. Shoemaker
Rocky Mountain Adventures,
Inc.
Dan Shoemaker
Rocky Mountain Whitewater
Patrick W. Doty
Rocky Outfitters
Rocky L. Niles
Rocky Point Outfitters
Orvall Kuester
Ron Mills Outfitting
Ronald E. Mills
Rose Ranch
Royal Outfitters
Tyrone L. Throop
Royal Trude Outdoor
Adventures
Mark J. Shutey
Ruby Springs Lodge
Paul & Jeanne Moseley
Rugg's Outfitting
Raymond Rugg
Rumph Ranch Outfitters
Richard N. Rumph
Running M Outfitters
Monte McLane
Running River Fly Guide
Stuart W. Howard
Running Waters Ranch
Bruce E. Funk
Rus Willis Outfitting
Richard K. Willis
Rush's Lake View Ranch
Kevin Rush
Rush's Lake View Ranch
Keith S. Rush
Russ Willis Outfitting
Richard K. Willis
**S & W Outfitters**
**Brad D. Hanzel**
S.W. Montana Fishing Co.
David V. Marsh
Sage & Sun Outfitting
David J. Patts
Salmon & Magruder Mountain
Outfitters
Don Habel
Salmon Forks Outfitters
William H. Tidwell
Sanfort & Sun Outfitting
Gregory F. Sanford
Saunders Floating
William C. Saunders

Scapegoat Wilderness Outfitter
William M. Plante
Schneider's Guide Service
Kenneth LeRoy Schneider
Scoffield Ranch Outfitters
George B. Scoffield
SE Alaska Outfitters
Thomas T. Zwick
Selway-Magruder Outfitters, Inc.
Kendall Lee Wells
Selway Bitterroot Outfitters
Dave Hettinger
Seven Bar Cross Ranch
Dale W. Williams
Seven Lazy P Guest Ranch
Charles C. & Sharon Blixrud
Shadow Basin Outfitters
Troy Ginn
Sherwood Outfitting
John Sherwood
Shields Valley Outfitters
Gregory L. Cissel
Shining Mountain Outfitters
Paul K. Johnson
Shining Times Outfitting
Richard Steve Vetsch
Shiplet Ranch Outfitters
Bob Shiplet
Shores Outfitting
Eric R. Shores
Sierra Safaris Wilderness Tours
Carl Swoboda
Silver Bow Outfitters
Leonard Howells
Silverwolf Chalet Resort
James & Bonnie Kennedy
Simpson Outfitters, Inc.
Mike W. Simpson
Skalkaho Ldge. Outftr. & Guides
John V. Rose
Skyline Guest Ranch & Guide
Victor Jackson
Skyline Guide Service, Inc.
Victor J. Jackson
Skyline Outfitters & Wilderness Lodge
Cameron E. Lee
Skyview Ranch
Sleepy Hollow Lodge
Larry P. Miller
Slip & Slide Guide Service
Franklin J. Rigler
Snowline Outfitters
Patrick G. Sinclair
Snowy Range Ranch Outfitters
Patrick R. Landers
Snowy Springs Outfitters
Shawn Little
South Fork Lodge
Southwest Montana Flies
Sphinx Mountain Outfitting
Gregory J. Doud
Spotted Bear Ranch
Kirk & Cathy Gentry
Spotted Bear Ranch
H. William Armstrong
Stan Fisher Outfitter & Guide
Stanley Fisher
Steve Fillinger Outfitters, Inc.
Steve Fillinger
Stillwater Outfitting & Guide Service
Brian Tutvedt
Stillwaters Outfitting
Lee R. Scherer
Stockton Outfitters
Billy D. Stockton
Story Cattle Co & Outfitting
Michael Story
Sugarloaf Mountain Outfitters
William Ray Flanagan

Summit Station Lodge
Sun Canyon Lodge
Lee Carlbom
Sun Dog Outfitters
Daniel L. Lahren
Sun Raven Guide Service
Katherine Howe
Sun Trek Outfitters
John J. Humble
Sunburst Adventures
Terry C. Johnson
Sundance Ranch
Sundown Outfitters
Lyle G. Reynolds
Sunrise Outfitters
Mark Daly
Sunset Guest Ranch
Mike C. McCormick
Swan Valley Llamas
Sweet Grass Ranch
Bill & Sally Carroccia
Sweetcast Angler
Steve Pauli
T Lazy B Ranch
Robert L. Walker
Tal Camp/Alaska Flyfishing
Tom Lerot
Tamarack Lodge
William A. McAfee
Tamarack Lodge
William A. McAfee
Tate's Upper Canyon Ranch
Donna & Jake McDonald
Tate's Upper Canyon Ranch
Donna & Jake McDonald
Teller Wildlife Refuge
Mary Stone
The Clearwater Crossing Lodge
Todd Earp
**The Complete Fly Fisher**
**David W. & Stuart Decker**
The Elkhorn Guest Ranch
The Fishhook
Dominic "Dee" Carestia
The Lodge
John Talia
The Missouri River Trout Shop & Lodge
The Montana Trout Club
Greg Lilly
The Old Kirby Place
**The Reflective Angler**
**Eric W. Troth**
The Rising Wolf Ranch
The River's Edge
David W. Corcoran
The Seventh Ranch
The Stevensons'
Harold R. Stevenson
The Stoney Lonesome Ranch
The Tackle Shop
Tim Combs
The Tom Miner Lodge
John A. Keenan
The Wald Ranch
The Yellowstone Fisherman
Kent B. Lombard
Think Wild Enterprises
Eugene G. Clark
Thompson's Angling Adventures
Howard A. Thompson
Thompson Outfitters, Inc.
Teddy Thompson
Thunder Bow Outfitters
Mike Robinson
Timber Creek Ranch
Dick Iverson
Timberline Outfitters
Willis L. Newman
**Tite Line Fishing**
Tom's Guide Service

Tom A. Bugni
Toussaint Ranch
Track Outfitters & Guide Service
Johnny C. McGee
Trapper Creek Outfitters
John A. Metz
Treasure State Outfitting
Michael J. Canavan
Tri Mountain Outfitters
Andy Celander
TriMountain Outfitters
Andy Celander
**Triple B Outfitters**
**David L. Gill**
Triple Creek Outfitters
Roy G. Ereaux
Triple Creek Ranch
Triple Creek/Thunder Bow
Charlotte A. Zikan
Triple M Outfitters
Mark J. Faroni
Triple Tree Ranch
William L. Myers
Troilus Kennels & Guide Service
Trout Fishing Only
William M. Abbot
Troutfitters
Frank M. Stanchfield
Trouthawk Outfitters
Randolph R. Scott
Troutwest
Thomas J. Laviolette
Twin Buttes Outfitters
Paul Mobley
Twitchell Bros. Snap Creek Ranch
J. Twitchell
Two Leggins Outfitters
David C. Schaff
Upper Canyon Outfitters
Donna Tate MacDonald
Valley View Ranch
Richard Gondeiro
Vanhaur Polled Hereford Ranch
Victor Colvard Guided Fly Fishing
Victor H. Colvard
Vikings Mountain Ranch
Douglas K. Knutson
Voyaguers of the Roche Jaune
Tom White
Wapiti Fine Flies & Outfitting
Jack Mauer
Warrens' Bunky Ranch
DeVon E. Warren
Wayne Hill Outfitting
Wayne Hill
Wellborn Bros.
Joseph P. Wellborn
Wellborn Bros.
David A. Wellborn
West Fork Meadows Ranch, Inc.
West Fork Outfitters
Ronald M. Corr
Western AK Sport Fishing
August & Kim Egdorf
Western Guide Services
Randy L. Walker
Western Rivers
Fred J. Tedesco
Western Timberline Outfitters
Jammin D. Krebs
**Western Waters**
**Gerald Rodger Nichols**
Whiskey Ridge Outfitter's
Steven R. Knox
Whitcomb Lodge
White Buffalo Ranch Retreat
**White Tail Ranch Outfitters /**

**WTR Outfitters, Inc.**
**Jack E. Hooker**
Whitefish Lake Fishing
Jim Crumal
Why Lazy Tee Ranch
Wickens Salt Creek Ranch
Wild Country Outfitters, Inc.
Jerry E. Strong
Wild Horizons Expeditions
Wild River Adventures
Bob Jordan
Wild River Adventures
Robert Y. Jordan
**Wild Rockies Tours**
**Gail Gutsche**
Wild Trout Outfitters
John F. Herzer
Wild Trout Outfitters
Jeffery D. Bingman
**Wild West Outfitters**
**Michael A. Goyins**
Wilderness Connection, Inc.
Charles G. Duffy
Wilderness Lodge & Skyline Outfitters
Cameron E. Lee
Wilderness Lodge Ltd.
Gregory C. Grabacki
Wilderness Outfitters
John Everett Stoltz
Wilderness Outfitters
Arnold D. Elser
Wilderness Riders Outfitting
Bruce J. Duffalo
Wildlife Adventures, Inc.
Jack E. Wemple
Williams Guide Service
Don A. Williams
Williams Outfitters
Harry L. Williams
Willow Ranch
Storrs M. Bishop
Willow Springs Outfitters
Gordon L. Patton
Wings of Adventure
Jeff Conners
Wolf Creek Guide Service
Steve Butts
Wolf Creek Shooting Preserve
Wolf Mountain Ranch
Wolfpack Outfitters
Jeffrey Wingard
Wolverine Guide Service
Richard A. Labert
Wolverton Outfitters
Keith Wolverton
World Class Outfitting Adventures
Larry & Carolyn Clinkenbeard
Jason D.
WRP Fly Fishing Outfitters
Bill Page
WTR Outfitters, Inc.
Jack & Karen Hooker
WW Outfitters
William A. White
X-A Ranch
Boland Clark
X Bar A Ranch
Pete Clark
Yaak River Outfitters
Patrick "Clint" Mills
Yellowater Outfitters
Roy G. Olsen
Yellowstone Catch & Reease Outfitter
Gary David Clount
Yellowstone Fly Fisher
Mike Sprague
Yellowstone International Fly
Yellowstone Llamas
William Gavin
Yellowstone Mountain Guides

Steven R. Gamble
Yellowstone Raft Co.
Chris Lyness
Yellowstone Raft Co.
Julia Page
Yellowstone River Hunting
Scott A. Cornell
Yellowstone Troutfitters
Yellowstone Valley Ranch
Z Bar J Outfitters
Mark Story
ZAK Inn Guest Ranch
ZW Ranch
Lorrie Zimdars

# NEW MEXICO

Jesse Gonzales
Martin Moismann
Cecil Kite
Donald S. Haggitt
Andy F. Valerio
Terrell Shelley
Robert M. Ortiz
Evan Lewis
Tom K. Klumker
Bill McKnight
Patrick Wantland
Martin D. Serna
Dirk Neal
Jim Worthan
4C's Guides & Outfitters
Chet Connor
5 M Outfitters
Bruce Maker
AAA Outfitters
Andrew & Annie Gonzales
Adventures in the Great
Outdoors
Tom Schubring
Al Johnson Outfitters
Al Johnson
All American Adventures
Dee Charles
All American Outfitter/Guide
Service
Gaudelli Brandon
ASAP Excavation
Paul Petersen
Baca Outfitters, Inc.
David Collis
Back Country Hunts
Steve Jones
Back Country Outfitters of
New Mexico
Sydney Cates
Baldy Mountain Outfitters
H. Gary Blacksten
Bar X Bar Ranch
Bear Creek Adventures
Eric Roybal
Bear Creek Outfitters
Louis Probo
Beartrack Hunting Consultants
John Abernathy
Beaverhead Outfitters
Ken C. Swaim
Beaverhead Outfitters
Jack Diamond
Big Canyon Outfitters
J. David Smoker
Black Range Guide &
Outfitting Service
Sterling Carter
Blackfork Flyfishing Guest
Ranch
Mickey & Maggie Greenwood
Blue Mountain Outfitters
Bob Atwood
Bobcat Pass Wilderness

Adventures
Henry Lewis
Born 'N' Raised on the San
Juan River
Tim R. Chavez
Boyd's High Timber Hunting
Richard (Buzz) Boyd
Brazos River Ranch
Ron Prieskorn
Bull Creek Outfitters
John R. Lucero
Bulls of Baldy Mountain Guide
Service
Art MackInstry
Bullseye Outfitter & Guide
Joseph Graham
Burnt Canyon Outfitter &
Guiding Service
John Allen
Butler - Moreno Ranch West
Bobby & Ginni Butler
Cactus Hunting Service
Jon Corn
Canadian River Cattle Co.
Joe Roy Ray
**Cecil Ralston Guide &
Outfitters**
**Cecil & Jodie Ralston**
Chama River Outfitters
Bob Ball
Chama Trophy Hunts
Jerry Kelley
Charlie's Sporting Goods
Circle Bar West Ranch
Tony G. Dickinson
Circle J Guiding Service
J.R. Rodella
Circle S Stables
Kirk Storey
Copper Country Outfitters
Steven C. Harvill
Cottonwood Anglers
Paul (Dave) Jacquez
Cougar Mountain Guide
Service
Doug Dobbs
Cougar Mountain Outfitters
Robert J. Seeds
CS Ranch Hunting & Outfitting
Randy Davis
Dark Canyon Outfitters
Howard (Butch) Harris, Jr.
Dark Timber
Randy Pettingill
Derringer Outfitters
David & Susan Derringer
Derringer Outfitters & Guides
David & Susan Derringer
Dirk Neal's Outfitting Service
Dirk Neal
Double A Outfitters
Andrew Sanchez
**Double J Outfitters**
Down Home
Walter Hobbs
E.J. Sceery Co.
Ed Sceery
East Moreno Ranch
Albert Murray & Ron Simmons
Elmer-Nelson Trophy
Outfitters
Bill Elmer
Elmer-Nelson Trophy
Outfitters
William B. Nelson
Far Flung Adventures
Steve Harris
Four Corners Guides &
Outfitters
Ted Stiffler
Garrison Guide & Outfitting
Gary Garrison
Garrison Guide & Outfitting

Gary Garrison
Gary Webb Guide & Outfitter
Gary Webb
Geronimo's Outfitters
David M. Jiron
Gila Hotsprings Ranch
Becky Campbell
Gila Wilderness Lodge
Robert Rawlins
Gila Wilderness Outfitters
Junior Lewis
Gonzales Outfitting
Thomas Gonzales
Gonzales Outfitting Guiding
Thomas Gilbert Gonzales
Govina Canyon Outfitters
Coy Craig
Green Gap Ranch
Mike Hansen
Guide & Outfitting Service
Ken Cason
H-J Outfitters
Elvin Post
H & A Outfitters
Andrew Salgado
Halfmoon Outfitters
Dr. Mike Jones
Hamwood Guide & Outfitters
Marty Greenwood
Handrich Guide & Outrfiters
Dave Handrich
**Hartley Guest Ranch**
**Doris Hartley**
Henderson Outfitters
Wesley Henderson
Hi Valley Outfitters, Inc.
Pres. Bill Wright
High Country Outfitters
Anthony B. Montoya
High Country Outfitters
Vance Lewis
High Country Store
Larry M. Sellers
High County Connections
Casey Veach
High Desert Angler
High Lonesome Outfitters
Kerry Sebring
High Mountain Outfitters
Pete Trujillo
High Mountain Outfitters
Pete Trujillo
Higher Ground Outfitters
Doc Rolston
Horizon Guide & Outfitters
Kelly Dow
Horse Quarter's, Inc.
Jack McCormick
JC Outfitters
Frank Casaus
Jenco Outfitters
Philip Zwiefelhofer
Jicarilla Apache Tribe
Jicarilla Game & Fish Dept.
Jim Bobb Guide & Outfitter
James Bobb
Ken Armenta Guide &
Outfitting
Ken Armenta
Kennedy Hunting Services
Kirk Kennedy
Kiowa Hunting Service
Tim Barraclough Jr. & Al Cata
Kiowa Hunting Service, Inc.
Alfred H. Cata
Kit Carson Outfitters
Darrell Bays
Known World Guide Service
John Weinmeister
Kokopelli Rafting Adventures
Jon Asher
L.J. Armstrong Big Game
Outfitter

L.J. Armstrong
Lazy BW Outfitters
Bob Ward
Limestone Outfitters
Chip Welty
Limestone Outfitters
Darell Welty
Little Rio Grande Outfitters
Edward T. Duran
Lone Pine Hunting & Outfitters
Jack Wyatt
Lonesome Dove
H.R. & Brandi Tomlin
Los Rios Anglers, Inc.
Lyons Ranch
Patrick Lyons
M-Lazy-A-Ranch Outfitter/
Guide Service
Robert Archibeque
M & M Outfitting
Michael Montoya
Mangas Outfitters
Mangas Outfitters
Tim Geng
Mark Upshaw Guide Service
Mark Upshaw
Mark V. Guide Services
Mike Archuleta
Martin Mosimann Hunting
Service
Martin Mosimann
Martinez Outfitters & Guide
Service
Donald Martinez
**Maynard Ranch**
Michael Root's Guide Service
Michael Root
Milligan Brand Outfitting
Marvin N. Henry Jr.
Mimbres Outfitters
Mark Miller
Mimbres Taxidermy & Guide
Service
William H. Lee
Montana Del Oso Ranch, Inc.
Tim Edwards
Moreno Valley Outfitters
Robert Reese
Moreno Valley Outfitters
Robert Reese & Mike Bucks
Morris Mosimann's Hunting
Service
Morris Mosimann
Mountain States Guide Service
Rob Degner
Mountain View Cabins/Eagle
Nest Marina
Jo Finley
Navajo Safari Outfitters
Charles Welch
New Mexico Prof. Big Game
Hunting
Mike Chapel
New Wave Rafting Co.
Steve Miller
Nine Sixteen Ranch Guide/
Outfitter
Terrell Shelley
NM Hunt & Hounds, Inc.
Andrew DeSalvo
NM Professional Big Game
Hunting, Inc.
Mike Chapel
North American Outfitters
Northern New Mexico Elk
Hunts
Mike Lopez
Northern NM Elk Hunts
Michael Lopez
NRA Whittington Center
Mike Ballew
Oso Ranch & Lodge
John & Pamela Adamson

Oso Ranch & Lodge
John & Pamela Adamson
Outwest Anglers
Brian Klein
P Diamond J Outfitters
R.J. Nolen
Percha Creek Outfitters
W.A. Williams
Point Blank Hunts
Joseph Jakab
Pound Bros. Guides &
Outfitters
Billy Jack Pound
Puerto Ranch Outfitting
Aparcio Herrera
**Pusch Ridge Outfitters**
Rawhide Outfitters
Rodney Prince
RB Outfitters & Guide Service
Ronald Schalla
Redwing Outfitters
Bob Daugherty
Reid Hollo Enterprises
Reid Hollo
Repair Altenatives Co.
Connie & Kreg Polzin Donald
Reserve Outfitters & Guides
Bill Jernigan
Ric Martin's Trophy
Adventures
Ric Martin
Rimrock Guides & Outfitters
Bryan K. Adair
Rio Brazos Outfitters
Frank Y. Simms
Rio Costilla Park
Rio Nutrias Cattle & Hunting
Juan Montano
Rio Penasco Hunting Service
Marvin Samford
Rizuto's San Juan River Lodge
Peggy Harrell
RJO Brazos Outfitters, Inc.
Jeff D. Wood
Robert I. Hooten
Robert I. Hooten
Rocky Mountain Big Game
Hunts
Jan Brown
Ross Johnson Pro. Big Game
Outfitter
Ross Johnson
Runnels Outfitter Guide
Service
Robert Runnels
Sagebrush Outfitters
Robert Guerin, Jr.
San Francisco River Outfitters
Tom Klunker
San Juan Troutfitters
Harry Lane
Sangre de Cristo Outfitters,
Inc.
Tony Herrera
Santa Fe Guiding Company
Robert B. King
Santa Fe Rafting ,Inc.
Russell Dobson
Santa Fe Stage Coach Line
Tim W. Carroll
Sibley Ranch
Christine Freeman
Sierra Grande Outfitters, Inc.
Leslie D. Ezell
Simpson Outfitters
Tom Simpson
Sky Ryders
Kurt J. Lee
Slim Randles Guide Service
Slim Randles
Soaring Eagle Outfitters
Sofia Outfitters
Roger Manning

South Fork Outfitters, Inc.
Michael Grace
South West Shot Gunners
Spill Ranch Hunting
Edward R. Spill
Sportsman Inn Guide Service
Stanley Hunting
Step Back Inn
Karen Rapp & Tweetie Blancett
Steve Cunico Hunting Services
Steve Cunico
Sure Strike Outfitters
Richard Ley
SW New Mexico Outfitters
Nettie Armstrong
SW Outfitters & Guide Service,
Ltd.
Robert A. Davis, Jr.
T-N-T Adventures
Joe M. Torrez Jr.
T-N-T Adventures
Joe M. Torrez, Jr.
Talisman Hunting
Charles Berg
Tall Tales Guide Services
Sara Jane Evans
Taos Outdoor Recreation
Assoc.
Taylor Streit Fly Fishing
Taylor Streit
**Terrero General Store and
Riding Stable Inc.**
**Huie Ley**
The Kauffman Group
Dennis R. Kauffman
The Lodge at Chama
Frank Simms
The Pueblo of Laguna
**The Reel Life**
**Manuel J. Monasterio**
The Santa Fe Flyfishing School
& Guide Ser.
Tierra Blanca Ranch Outfitters
Scott Chandler
Tierra Encantada Guide/
Outfitter
Roger Gabaldon
Timberline Outfitters
Jerry Cazares
**Timberline Outfitters**
**James (Perry) & Brenda
Hunsaker**
Tinnin Enterprises
Tomahawk Outfitters
James E. Kneip
Trail Riders
Susan Johnson
Trapper's Trophy Hunting
Vernon Langworthy
Trappers Trophy Hunting
Tri-Me Outfitter
Ronald Ulibarri
Trophy Striper Guide Service
Ronnie Orr
United States Outfitters, Inc.
George Taulman
Val's Trophy Hunts
Valdemar Deherrera, Jr.
Vermejo Park Ranch
Jim Baker
Vernon Tile
Walkers Trophy Outfitters
Jeremy Walker
Way West Outfitters
Keith Reiley
West Tex-New Mex Hunting
Services
Jess Rankin
Whitten's Outfitters & Guide
Service
Lewis Arnold Whitten
Zuni Mtn. Guide & Outfitting
Robert Fifer

# UTAH

Val Robb
Karen C. Lecount
Ken F. Kohlbrecher
Joy B. Tlou
Phil Baker
4 Mile Hunting Club
Adrift Adventures/Myke
Hughes
Myke Hughes
Adventure River Expeditions
Skip Bell
Alaska Travel
Tim Montroy
All 'Round Ranch
Wann Brown
Allen's Outfitters
Jeff Allen
Alpine Adventures
**Alpine Angler Fly Shop &
Boulder Mtn. Adventures**
**Rich & Lori Cropper**
Angler's Inn
Byron Gunderson
Bear River Outfitters, Inc.
Brad Ipsen
Beaver Creek Lodge
Beer Creek Farms
Big Foot Fly Shop
Big Rock Candy Mountain
River Trips
Black Mountain Outfitters
Marion Frandsen
Blindforl Guide Service
Ken & Cathy Church
Boulder Mountain Ranch
Katie Austin
Bucks & Bulls Guides &
Outfitters
Kim Bonnett
Buffalo Pointe, Inc.
Bugle Creek Outfitters
Jeff Jensen
Bugle Point Outfitters
Canyon Voyages
Don Oblak
Canyonlands by Night
Canyonlands Field Institute
Karla VanderZanden
CC Lodge & Outfitters
Cass Casper
Cedar Mountain Outfitters
Steve Sillitoe
Cedar Springs Marina
Chapoose Rivers & Trails
Circle E Outfitters
Randy Eames
Collett's Recreation Service,
Inc.
Colorado River & Trail
Expeditions
David Mackay
Cougar Country Outfitters &
Guide Service
Karen Lacunate
Cowboy Trails
Cowpie Backcountry
Adventures
Coyote Expeditions
Coyote Road
Dalton Gang Adventures
Deer Springs Ranch
Larry Clarkson
Defa's Dude Ranch
Diamond Bar Ranch
Ben Isaac
Dinosaur River Expeditions
Tim Mertens
Don & Meg Hatch River

Expeditions
Meg Hatch
Dry Creek Hunts
Bryce Pilling
Eagle Outdoor Sports
Eagle Outdoor Sports
Rex Mumford
Eagle Outdoor Sports
Doug Smith
Ed  Black Trail Rides
Falcon's Ledge Lodge/
Altamont Flyfishers
Five Mile Canyon Sporting
Club
Flaming Gorge Flying Service,
Inc.
Mark Brown
Flaming Gorge Lodge
Craig Collett
Flaming Gorge Recreation
Services
Herald Egbert
Flying "J" Outfitters
Lawny Jackson
Grand Canyon Bar 10 Ranch
Grand Canyon Expeditions Co.
Michael Denoyer
Great Salt Lake Waterfowlers
H & H Hunting
Bruce & Robert Hubbard
Hatt's Ranch
HCA Raft
Geoffrey D. Randle
High Desert Adventures, Inc.
Mark Sleight
Holiday River Expeditions
Dee Holladay
J/L Ranch Outfitter and Guides
Inc.
Linda & Joe Jessup
Jan's Mountain Outfitters
Jans Mountain Outfitters
Tina Quayle
Johnson Cattle Company
Brad Johnson
K.A. Guides & Outfitters
Kenneth A. Sorenson
Kar-McGee's Outdoor
Adventures
Ken Sleight Pack Trips
Ken Sleight
L & R Bird Ranch
L.C. Ranch
La Gracious Stables
La Sal Mountain Guest Ranch
Sunny & Hardy Red
Lake Powell Tours, Inc.
Mark
Lakeview Pheasantry
Leeder Hunting
Charles F. Leeder
Local Waters Flyfishing
Lochsa River Company
Gregory Bell
Mark Sleight Expeditions, Inc.
Mark Sleight
Moab Rafting Co.
Moki Mac River Expeditions
Anna Lee Quist
Monument Valley Trail Rides
Mosida
Mountain West Outfitters
Shane Dykster
Navajo County Guided Trail
Rides
Navtec Expeditions
John Williams & Chris Williams
Nichols Expeditions, Inc.
Judy Nichols
Nine Mile Ranch
North American River &
Canyonlands Tours
Old Moe Guide Service

Terry Collier & Timm Mertens
Outdoor Source
John Campbell
Outlaw Trails, Inc.
Pack Creek Ranch
Pack Saddle Trips
Passage to Utah
Peak River Expeditions
Pheasant Valley Hunting
Preserve
Pleasant Valley Hunting
Preserve
Porcupine Adventures Inc.
Roland Leishman
Quarter Circle "E" Outfitters &
Guest
Gail Eldridge
Quarter Circle E Guest Ranch
Rainy's Flies & Supplies
Red Creek Outfitters
Red River Canoe Co.
Bruce Keeler
Red Rock Adventure
Red Rock Outfitters
Red Rock River Co., Inc.
Red Rock River Co., Inc.
Steven Summers
Red Rockn' Llamas
Bevin E. McCabe
Redd Ranches
David Redd
Reid Ranch
Gardner Reid
River Hollow Hunting Club
Marsha Burbank
Road Creek Ranch
Rock Creek Guest Ranch
Gayle Gibbs
Rock Creek Ranch
Rock Creek Ranch, Corp.
Rocking "R" Ranch
Rocky C Adventures
Rocky Meadow Adventures
Rooster Valley Pheasants
Ruby's Outlaw Trail Rides
Ruby Ranch
Sagewood Outfitters
Justin Jones
San Rafael Trail Rides
Scenic Rim Trail Rides
Scenic Safaris
**Sheri Griffith Expeditions, Inc.**
Slickrock Adventures, Inc.
Spinner Fall Guide Service
Spirit Lake Lodge
George & Connie Coonradt
Sportsman's Paradise
Ed Horner
Tag-A-Long Expeditions
Bob Jones
Tanner Ranch
Tawanta Ranch
Monte Farnsworth
Ted Hatch River Expeditions,
Inc.
Ted Hatch
The Alternate Transit
Authority
The Flyfishers Den
Three Green Outfitters
James Ryan Stone
Totem Pole Tours & Trailrides
Tour West, Whitewater
Adventure
Trout Creek Flies
Dennis Breer
U-Bar Wilderness Ranch
Ugashik River Lodge, Inc.
Utah Escapades
Ute Indian Tribe
Fish & Game/Outfoor Rec.
Program
W.C. Flyers

Wasatch Outfitters & Guides
Western Mountain Outfitters
Dudley Henderson
Western River Expedition
Western River Expeditions
Western River Expeditions,
Inc.
Brian Merrill
Western Rivers Flyfisher
Wild Adventures
Wilderness Tracks
Harley Johnson
Willow Creek Kennels & Guide
Service
Kelly Laier
Willow Valley Sportsman
Dan Lockwood
World Wide River Expeditions
Richard Jones
Zion's Kolob Mountain Ranch
Zion's Ponderosa Resort

# WYOMING

Jim Gimpel
John A. Porter
Jeff Reynolds
Ridge W. Taylor
Dennis Edwards
Stephen Roberts
Joe Kalus
Chester F. Hejde
Dave Clarendon
Gene Wocicki
Peter Larsen
Joseph F. Mott
James R. Talbott
Thomas E. Schutte
George F. Hook
John E. Keiser
Tom R. Montgomery
46 Outfitters
R. Lane Turner
7D Ranch
Marshall Dominick
88 Ranch Outfitters
William Henry III/Robert
Henry
A Cross Ranch
Chuck Sanger
A J Brink Outfitters
James D. Brink
AA Outfitters
Ronald Ball
Absaroka Mountain Lodge
Absaroka Mountain Lodge
Resort
Dave & Cathy Sweet
Absaroka Ranch
Robert Budd Betts, Jr.
AJ Brink Outfitters
Jim Brink
AJ Outfitters
Jeffery HIll
Aladdin Outfitters
Walter Marchant
All American Outfitters
Forest Stearns
Allen's Diamond Four
Wilderness Ranch
Jim Allen
Antelope Outfitters
Steve Beilgard
Arizona Creek Outfitters
Roy Bonner
**Arrowhead Outfitters**
**Bobby Lowe**
Aspen Grove Ranch Outfittters
Frederick Neuman

Astle Hunting Camp
Boyd Astle
Aune's Absaroka Angler
C. Scott Aune
Autumn Meadows
Gary Dean Buck
B & B Outfitters
Brett Jones
B.J. Outfitters
James Ellison
Bald Mountain Outfitters, Inc.
Terry Pollard
Bar-J Ranch
Bar-T-Five, Inc.
Bar Diamond R Outfitters
Brad & Van Dana
Bare Tracks Trophies
Major F. Miller
Barker-Ewing River Trips
Frank Ewing
Barker-Ewing Scenic Float
Trips
Barlow Outfitting
Robert L. Barlow
BB Outfitters
Brian Beishers
Bear Basin Camp
Francis Fox
Bear Creek Hunting Camp
Francis Fox
Bear Lodge Outfitters
Kenneth Rathbun
Bear Mountain Back Trails
Bear Track, Inc.
Peter & Carey Dube
Beard Outfitters
Lyle Beard
Beartooth & Absaroka
Wilderness
Charles H. Smith
**Beaver Creek Outfitters**
**Steve Kobold**
Beaver Creek Outfitters
L.D.Gibertz
Beaver Trap Outfitters
Al Martin
BEST Adventures
Bobby Lowe
Big Horn Basin Outfitters
Ed R. Cormier
Big Horn Mountain Outfitters
Toby Johnson
Big Horn Outfitters
Bryce Antley
Big Horn Outfitters
John Nation
Big Rock Outfitters, Inc.
Randy Engler
Big Sandy Lodge
Bernard Kelly
Big Sandy Lodge
Bernard Kelly
Billings Enterprises
Ray Billings
Bitterroot Ranch
Bayard Fox
BJ Outfitters
William Hollingsworth
Blackwater Creek Ranch
Tom & Debbie Carlton
Bliss Creek Outfitters
Tim Doud & Doris Roesch
Bolten Ranch Outfitters
Robert Terrill
**Boulder Lake Lodge**
**Kim Bright**
Box K Ranch
Walter Korn
Box Y Hunting Lodge & Guest
Ranch
Ken Clark
Boxelder Trophies
Maurice Bush

Boysen Outfitters
William M. Weaver
Bressler Outfitter, Inc.
Joe Bressler
Bridger Teton Outfitters
Bridger Wilderness Outfitters
BridgerTeton Outfitters
Randy Foster
Broken Horn Outfitters
Rock Buckingham
Broken Horseshoe Outfitters
William Carr
Brooks Lake Lodge
Will Rigsby
Brush Creek Guest Ranch
Buckhorn Mountain Outfitters
Jerry Martin
Bud Nelson Outfitters
Bud Nelson
Buffalo Bill Cody FFA
Josh Stratman & Dan Benson
Buffalo Creek Outfitters
Otis Bloom
Butte Creek Outfitters
Theresa Lineberger
C Bar C Outfitters
Clifford J. Clark
C K Hunting & Fishing Camp
Darrell Copeland
Cabin Creek Outfitters
Duane Wiltse
Canyon Ranch Gun Club
Cash Outfitters
Douglas Cash
Castle Rock Ranch
Central Wyoming Archery
Outfitter
Kim Cooper
Cherokee Outfitters
Ivan L. Samson
Circle S Outfitters
Don Smith
Clear Creek Hunting
Mickie
Cody's Ranch Resort
Barbara Cody
Cole Creek Outfitters
Jon C. Nicolaysen
Coulter Creek Outfitters
Robert Johnson
Cowboy Village Resort
Cowpoke Outfitters
Jack Risner
Coy's Yellow Creek Outfitting
B. Joe Coy
Crandall Creek Outfitters
Bruce Hillard
Crescent H Ranch
Christy
Cross C Ranch & Outfitting
Willard M. Woods
Cross Milliron Ranch
Larry Miller
Crossed Sabres Ranch
Fred Norris
Crystal Creek Outfitters
Gap Puchi
D & D Outfitters
Dampier Hunting Lodge
James Dampier
Dan Kinneman Outfitter-
Guide
Daniel Kinneman
**Darby Mountain Outfitters**
**R. John Harper & Chuck**
**Thornton**
**Darwin Ranch, Inc.**
**Loring Woodman**
Dave Flitner Packing &
Outfitting
David Flitner
Dave Hanna Outfitters
Dave Hanna

Dave Hansen Whitewater
David Ranch
Melvin David
Deadman Creek Outfitters
Gregg Fischer
Deer Forks Ranch
Benny Middleton
Diamond D Ranch-Outfitters
Rod Doty
Diamond D Ranch Outfitters
Rod Doty
Diamond J Outfitters
Joe Stuemke
Diamond Tail Outfitters
Stan Filtner
Dick Page
Richard L. Page
Dodge Creek Ranch
Jerry Kennedy
Don ( Tip ) Tipton's Outfitting
Don K. Tipton
Don Scheer Outfitters
Don Scheer
Donkey Creek Outfitters
Steve R. Bietz
Double Diamond Outfitters
Reed "Rick" Miller
Double Diamond Outfitters
Craig Griffith
Double Diamond X Ranch
Dale Sims, Jr.
DT Outfitting
Ray Focht
Dull Knife Hunting
Kenneth Graves
Dunior Outfitters Corp.
George William Snodgrass
**Early Guest Ranch**
**Ruth & Wayne Campbell**
East Slope Outfitters
Steven A. Richards
East Table Creek Hunting
Camp
Kerry Chadwick
Eatons' Ranch
Jeff Way
Elephant Head Lodge
Phil & Joan Lamb
Elk Antler Outfitters
Richard Ashburn
Elk Mountain Outfitters
Myron J. Wakkuri
Elk Mountain Outfitters, LLC
Myron J. Wakkuri
Elk Ridge Outfitters
Terry Reach
Elk Ridge Outfitters & Lodge
Terry Reach
Equitour, Ltd.
Even Toe Outfitters
Phil Gonzales
Far Horizons Trophy Hunts
Raymond Hall
Fatboy Fishing
A.J. DeRosa
Five Star Expeditions, Inc.
Ed Beattie
Floyd Ranch Hunts
Herb Kretschman
Fly Shop of the Big Horns
Flying A Ranch
Debbie Hansen
Flying H Ranch
John and Amee Barrus
Flying S Outfitters
Kathleen M. Steele
Flying U Ranch
Ralph Foster
Flying W Horse Service, Inc.
Gordon C. White
Flying X Ranch
Earl (Sonny) Malley
Forest Dell Guest Ranch

Low & Ads Mae Gardner
Full Circle Outfitters
Buck Braten
Gary Fales Outfitting
Gary Fales
Gene Saltz Big Game Outfitting
Gene Saltz
General Outfitter
Ronald O. Titterington
Gilroy Outfitting
Paul Gilroy
Goff Creek Lodge Resort
Rick & Valerie Merrill
**Grand & Sierra Outfitter**
**Glen Knotwell**
Grand Slam Outfitters
Mark Condict
Granstorm Outfitters
Swede Granstorm
Grant Ranch Outfitters
Richard Grant
Grassy Lake Outfitters
Dan Blair
Great Rocky Mountain
Outfitters
Robert Smith
Green River Guest Ranch
Outfitters
Phillip Reints Jr.
Green River Outfitters
Bill Webb
**Greer Outfitters**
**Randy & Lora Greer**
Greysnest Mountain Retreat
Tent-Camp
Grizzly Outfitters
Cole Benton
Grizzly Ranch
Frank & Rick Felts
Gros Ventre River Ranch
Hack's Tackle & Outfitters
Haderlie's Tincup Mt. Guest
Ranch
David & Lorie Haderlie
Half Moon Lake Guest Ranch
Frank Deede
Hanna Outfitting
Dave Hanna
Hart Brothers Partnership
William Hart
Hayden & Sons Ranch
Troy Hayden
Heart Six Ranch
Joe Doudy
Hensley Trophy Outfitter
Rob Hensley
**Hidden Basin Outfitters**
**Phillip & George Engler**
Hidden Creek Outfitters
Bill Perry
Hidden Valley Ranch
Duaine & Sheila Hagen
High Country Flies
High Island Ranch & Cattle Co.
Karen Robbins
High Mountain Adventures
LaMont Merritt
High Mountain Horseback
Adventure
Fern White
High Mountain Outfitters
Robert Deroche
High Plains Pronghorns
Fazilath (Tim) Qureshi
Highland Meadow Outfitters
Mark Thompson
Hiland Outfitters
Don Bennett
Horse Creek Land Co.
Kenneth Neal
Hunton Creek Outfitters
Clark Noble
Indian Creek Outfitters

Bruce Moyer
Indian Summer Outfitters
Steve Robertson
International Blackpowder
Hunting Association
J & B Outfitters
Jim Fritz
J.T. Tinney Outfitting
James T. Tinney
Jack Creek Outfitters
Jackson's Hole Adventures
Jackson Hole Kayak School
Jackson Hole Llamas
Jackson Hole Mountain Guides
Andy Carson
Jackson Hole Whitewater
Jackson Peak Outfitters
Charlie M. Petersen, Jr.
Jenkins Hunting Camp
Larry Jenkins
Jensen Hunting Camp
Keith Jensen
Jiggs Pack & Guide Service
Jiggs Black
**John Henry Lee Outfitters**
**John Lee**
Johnson's A Bar One Ranch
Clyde Johnson
Johnson Outfitting
Dean Johnson
Jones Outfitters
Patrick Jones
K Bar Outfitting
John Buxton II
**K Bar Z Guest Ranch &**
**Outfitters**
**Dave Segall & Dawna Barnett**
Kedesh Guest Ranch
Charles Lander
Keighley's Camps
Mark Lantz
Kyle Wall's Trout Burn Guide
Service
Lander Llama Company
Scott Woodruff
Laramie Range Outfitters
John Bisbing
Larry Stetter, General Outfitter
Larry Stetter
Lazy BJ Outfitters
Bill Woodworth
Lazy L & B Ranch
Lee & Bob Naylon
Lazy TX Outfitting
Clayton W. Voss
Let's Gallop Horseback
Adventures/Sandy Gap Ranch
Frank Deede & Kerry Thomas
Lewis & Clark River
Expeditions
**Lightning Creek Ranch**
**Jim  & Dawna Werner**
Linn Brothers Outfitting
Eugene Linn
Little Bighorn Outfitters
Tim Moyes
Little Sunlight Outfitters
Don J. Vitto
Llano Outfitters
John F. Savini
Lone Pine Sports
Bart & D'Ann Wilkes
Lone Wolf Outfitters
Bambi Schumacher
Lost Creek Outfitters
Ron & Kathi Clark
Lost Creek Ranch Resorts
Mike & Bev Halpin
**Lozier's Box "R" Ranch**
**Levi M. Lozier**
Lund Outfitting
Kurt W. Lund
M & M Outfitters

Mark K. Teel
M.F. Hunting
Larry Feuz
Mad River Boat Trips
Breck O'Neill
Magic Mountains Outfitters
S.(Sharon) R. Dayton
Majo Ranch
Grant Stambaugh
Mangis Guide Service
Klay Mangis
Mankin Wildlife
James R. Mankin
McNell & Sons
Merrill McNell
Medicine Bow Drifters
Medicine Bow Outfitters
Harold Embree
Merritt's Buckhorn Ranch
Lamont & Shirley Merritt
Mike Smith Outfitters
Michael Smith
Mill Iron Ranch
Chancy Wheeldon
Milliron 2 Outfitting
Billy Sinclair
Mooncrest Outfitters, Inc.
Robert Model
Moose Creek Ranch
Moose Head Ranch
Nelson Outfitting
David & Dennis Nelson
North Fork Anglers
North Fork Outfitters
Jim VanNorman
North Laramie Outfitting &
Guide
Allen L. Cook
North Rim Outfitters
Roy Gamblin
Northern Wyoming Outfitters
George K. Warner
NX Bar Ranch
Brian MacCarty
Old Glendevey Ranch, Ltd.
Garth Peterson
Open Creek Outfitting
John Billings
Outfitters Unlimited
Todd Jones
Outwest Safari Unlimited
Gene Carrico
**P Cross Bar Ranch**
**Marion & Mary Scott**
Pahaska Tepee
Bob Coe
Paintrock Adventures-
Outfitters Unlimited
Todd Jones
Paintrock Outfitters
William F. Craft
Papoose Peak Outfitters
Louis Cary
Paradise Guest Ranch
Jim Anderson
Paradise Ranch Co.
James Anderson
Pass Creek Outfitters
Richard Miller
Pat Garrett Outfitter
Pat Garret
Pathfinder Outfitters & Guides
Greg Burgess
Pennoyer Outfitting
George Pennoyer
Petersen Outfitting
Greg Petersen
Peterson's Hunting Camps
Everett D. & Pat Peterson
Pheasant Meadows Gun Club
Pilgrim Creek Hunting Camp
John Watsabaugh
Pine Creek Outfitters

Earl Wright
Piney Creek Outfitters
Ron Reece
Platt's Guides & Outfitters
Ronald R. Platt
Powder Horn Outfitters
Darwin Powers
Powder River Breaks Outfitters
Glenn Sorenson
Powder River Outfitters
John Francis
Preemption Creek Hunts
Ralph Abell
Press Stephens-Outfitter
Press Stephens
Professional Big Game
Outfitters
Bud Nelson
Pronghorn Adventures
Greg Salisbury
Pumpkin Buttes Outfitters
Bill Bruce Hines
R Lazy S Ranch
Bob & Claire McConaughty
R.E. Evans Grizzly Creek
Outfitters
Richard Evans
Rafter B Outfitters
Larry Brannian
Rand Creek Outfitters
Ron McCloud
Rand Creek Ranch
Kevin & Darlene Lauer
Ranger Creek Ranch
Claude A. Powell
Raven Creek Outfitters
Kent Drake
Rawah Ranch
Pete Kunz
Red Cloud Outfitting
Brett L. Sorenson
**Red Desert Outfitters**
**Vic Dana**
Red Rock Ranch
Red Valley Outfitters
Mike Wolcott
Reel Women Fly Fishing
Adventures
Rendezvous Outfitters
Bruce Blanthorn
Ridgemaster Outfitting
Charles Cureton
Rim Rock Hunts
Lee Miller
Rimrock Dude Ranch
Gary & Dede Fales
Rimrock Hunts
Dan Artery
Ritz Sporting Goods
**River S Enterprises**
RNR Rainbows N Racks
Raymond Stroup
Rocking L-H
Larry J. Henry
Rocky Butte Outfitters
Ed G. Schaffer
Rocky Mountain Horseback
Vacations
Rocky Mountain Wilderness
Adventures
Rocky Top Lion Outfitters
Scott Q. Schroer
Romios Outfitters
Pete Romios
Ron Dube's Wilderness Adv.
Ron Dube
Ronell Skinner Guide &
Outfitters
Ronell Skinner
Rough Country Outfitters &
Guides
James D. Schell
S N S Outfitters & Guide

Service
SY Gilliland
Sagebrush Outfitters
Don Hockett
Sand Creek Outfitters
Jim P. Collins
Sand Wild Water, Inc.
Charles Sands
Sanke River Kayak & Canoe
School
Saratoga Safaris
Tim Barkhurst
Savage Run Outfitters
James F. Talbott
Schively Ranch
Schmalz Outfitting
Don Schmalz
Seven D Ranch
Nikki & Marshall Dominick I.
Ward
Seven J Outfitters
Jeffery L. Smith
Sheep Mesa Outfitters
Ronald Good
Sheep Mountain Outfitters
Tim Haberberger
Shirley Mountain Outfitters
Steve Steinle
Shoal Creek Outfitters
Scott Millward
Shoshone Lodge Outfitters &
Guest Ranch
Keith Dahlem
Simons Hunting Camp
Frank Simons
Skinner Brothers Outfitters
Robert Skinner
Sleeping Indian Outfitters
Paul Crittenden
Snake River Fishing Trips
Snake River Institute
Snake River Outfitters
Thomas Grieve
Snake River Park, Inc.
Stan & Karen Chatham
Snyder Outfitting
Stanley Snyder
Solitary Angler
Van Beacham
Solitude Float Trips, Inc.
Southern Wyoming Outfitters
Dale Pribyl
Southfork Double Diamond X
Ranch
Dale W. Sims
Spear-O-Wigwam Ranch
James Niner
Spearhead Ranch
Frank N. Moore
Sports Lure
Spotted Horse Ranch
Clare Berger
Spotted Horse Ranch
Dick Bess
Squaw Creek Ranch &
Outfitters
Gail Zimmerman
Star Valley Outfitters
Reed S. Clark
Steve Sheaffer Outfitters
Steve & Connie Sheaffer
Suda Outfitters
Wayne Suda
Sully Outfitters
Sully Simons
Sunrise Outfitters
Mike Heins
Sweetwater Fishing
Expeditions
George H. Hunker
Sweetwater Gap Ranch
Robert Wilmetti
Sweetwater Outfitters

Ray A. Dennis
**Swift Creek Outfitters**
**B.J. & Vicki Hill**
Swift Creek Outfitters
Therese Metherell
T Cross Ranch
Ken & Garey Neal
**T Lazy T Outfitters**
**Tom Toolson**
Table Mountain Outfitters
Dale Critchfield
Tally-Ho Outfitters
Allan Perry
Taylor Outfitters
Tory Taylor
Taylor Ranch & Outfitting
Glenn B. Taylor
Teton Crest Outfitters
Phil Major
Teton Wilderness Outfitting
Nate C. Vance
The Beartree Brand Range
Riders
Roger & Bonnie Preston
The Head Hunters
Don C. Malli
The Hideout/Flitner Ranch
Kathryn Flitner
The HOLE Hiking Experience,
Inc.
Cathy Shill
The Last Resort
Dru Roberts
The Lodges of East Yellowstone
Valley
The Tackle Box
Dean Coy
The Trophy Connection
Julia Dube
Thompson Outfitters
Dick Thompson
Thunder Mountain Outfitters
Cameron Garnick
Thunder Ridge Outfitters
Ron Morrison
Timberline Outfitters
Craig P. Oceanak
Top Two Ocean Pass Ranch &
Outfitting
John Winter
Tracker, Packer & Guide
Outfitting
Gary Dean Talbott
Trail Creek Ranch
Ms. Alex Menolescino
Trail Inn & Motel
Marian & Tina Duda
Trails West Outfitters
Robert Sundeen
Trails West Outfitters
Roger St. Clair
Trefren Outfitters
Tim & Sharon Trefren
**Triangle C Ranch**
**Cameron W. Garnick**
Triangle X Ranch
Donald Turner
Triple Creek Hunts
Jim Freeburn
Triple Three Outfitters
J. Craig Smith
Trophy Chasers Outdoor Adv.
Mark Lantz
Trophy Connection
Trophy Outfitters
Dwight N. Heater
Turpin Meadow Ranch
Stan Castagno
**Twin Pine Ranch**
**Larry & Peg Gerke**
Two Bars Seven Ranch
Two Ocean Pass Outfitting
John R. Winter

UL Ranch Outfitters
Jerry R. Palm
Ullery Outfitters
Brad Ullery
UpStream Anglers & Outdoor
Adventures
UXU Ranch
Hamilton Bryan
V Bar F Cattle Co.
Neal R. Schuman
Wade's Piney Creek Outfitting
Bobbi Wade
Wayne Graves Outfitters
Wayne Graves
West Laramie Fly Store
Westbank Anglers
Western Cross Outfitters
Kym L. Taylor
Western Wyoming Outfitters
Jerry Thune
**Western Wyoming Trophy**
**Hunts**
Whiskey Mountain Outfitters
Gari Epp
Whitetail Creek Outfitters
Raymond M. Hulse
Wild Game Outfitters
Paul Strausner
Wildcat Outfitters
Pat Phillipps
Wilderness Trails
Galloway M. Clover
Wind River Mountain
Outfitters
Fritz Meyer
Wind River Mt. Lion Outfitters
James D. Rice
Wind River Outfitters
Kim Merchant
Wind River Ranch
Arthur Davenport
Windy Peak Outfitters
Darin Geringer
Wolf Lake Outfitters
Mike Nystrom
Wolf Mountain Outfitters
Guy Azevedo
Wolverine Creek Outfitters
Warren Fleming
Wycon Safari, Inc.
Wynn Condict
Wyoming's Choice
Dick Vandeveer
Wyoming Big Horn Sheep
Hunts
Stanley Siggins
Wyoming Country Outfitters
Kevin McNiven
Wyoming Dark Timber Adv.
Dave Parrish
Wyoming Peak Outfitters
Wyoming Professional Hunters
Jay Lesser
Wyoming Rivers & Trails
Liz & Matt David
Wyoming Trophy Hunts
Kenneth Metzler
Wyoming Trophy Outfitters
Randy & Sharon Brown
Wyoming Wilderness
Outfitters
Jake Kay Clark
Yellowstone Outfitters
Gary Caskey
Yellowstone Outfitters
Lynn & Marcene Madsen
Yellowstone Outfitters Hunting
& Fishing
Lynn Madsen
Yellowstone Troutfitters
Steve Perry
ZN Outfitters
George Williams

# CANADA
# ALBERTA

Nayda Hallett
Dave Unger
Darrell Baird
Irvin Palmer
Ted A. Horechka
Roger A. Lee
Robert Stafford
Glen Willsie
Access - Alberta Outfitting &
Guide Service
Michael Terry
Alberta Bighorns
RW Bobby Turner
Alberta Bowhunting
Adventures
Ted Hansen
Alberta Bush Adventures
Richard Deslauriers
Alberta Frontier Wilderness
Adventures
Judy & Ed Walker
Alberta Native Guide Service
Ken Steinhauer
Alberta Native Guide Services
Ken Steinhauer
Alberta Rocky Mountain Trail
Adv.
K&M Robinson & L&M Nielson
Alberta Trophy Hunters &
Outfitters
Richard Page
Alberta Whitetail Connection
Don Tyschuk
Alberta Wilderness Guide
Service
David Bzawy & Terry Birkholz
All-Terrain Guide & Outfitting
Ronald Bell
Alstott Outfitting
Edwin Alstott
Amethyst Lakes/Tonquin
Valley Pack Trips
Wald & Lavone Olson
Anchor D Guiding & Outfitting
Dewy & Jan Matthews
Anchor D High Mountain
Hunts
Anchor D High Mountain
Hunts, Ltd.
Dewy Matthews
Andrew Lake Lodge
Glen Wettlaufer
Andrew Lake Lodge & Camps
Athabasca River Outfitters
Bryan Radke & Bruce
Wierenga
Babala Stone Sheep Outfitters,
Ltd.
Randy Babala
Bar JJ Outfitting
Jim & Connie Kelts
Barrier Mountain Outfitters
A. H. Johnson
Battle River Lodge
Nick Frederick
BBD Guiding & Outfitting
Dave Moore
Bearpaw Outfitting
Scott Taylor
Beaverhill Outfitters
Brent Reil
**Big Rack Adventures**
**Blair & Kathy Trout**
Big Smoky Outfitting, Ltd.
Gary & Ricki Kruger
Bittern Lake Outfitters
Kevin Rolfe
Black Dog Outfitters

Blaine Burns
Blue Bronna Guiding &
Outfitting
Glenn Brown
Blue Ridge Outfitters
Wynder & Billl Barrus Dee
Boss Guiding Services
Bob Byers
Boss Guiding Services
Bob Byers & Ross
Scheerschmidt
Bow River Troutfitters
Brewster Mountain Packtrain
Broadhead Outfitters
Kent Butterfield
Buck 'n Bears Outfitters
Wendell Mann
Buck Mountain Outfitters
Merv Purschke
Buckbrush Outfitters
Rod Hunter
Buffalo Lake Outfitters
Brad Steinhoff
Canadian Hunting Co.
Dean Yardley
Cheemo Lodge
Ed Granger
Chester Sands Outfitting
Chester Sands
Chimney Creek Outfitters
Miles & Joanne Stern
Chinchaga River Hunts
Dennis Potter
Classic Outfitters
Jim Hole Jr.
Cook & Sands Ranch
Bill Sand & Sons
Cougar Outfitters
John Cassidy & Mark Tannas
Cree Lake Lodge
Vern & Gerri Biller
Cypress Expeditions
Lyle Czember
D & S Guiding
Robert Dean Cumming
DeBolt Guiding & Outfitting
Ian & Hugh Alexander
DeBolt Guiding & Outfitting
Hugh Alexander
Del Bredeson Guiding &
Outfitting
Del Bredeson
Diamond And-A-Half
Outfitters
Bill Sinclair
Diamond Jim & Sons Mountain
Rides
Jim Colosimo
Diamond Outfitters
Byron Tofteland
Don Ayers Outfitters
Don & Tuffy Ayers
Double Diamond Outfitters
Gordon Burton
Double Diamond Wilderness
Trails
John & Jeramy Hatala
Double H Outfitters
Herb & Heather Bailey
Echo Canyon Outfitters, Ltd.
Graham Perry
Elk Island Outfitters
Bernd Light
Eric's Wilderness
Eric Twardzilk
Excell Outfitters
Al Schulz
Folding Mountain Outfitters
Dale Drinkall
Frank Kuhnen
Frank Kuhnen
Frontier Fishing Lodge
Wayne Witherspoon

George Kelly Outfitters
George Kelly
Glacier Peak Adventures
Nancy Koopman
Goffitt River Outfitters
Rod E. Roth
Golden Bear Outfitting
Eldon Hoff
Granger's Cheemo Lodge
Clayton Granger
Great Bear Adventures, Ltd.
Ken Cotterill
Great North Outfitters
Neil Wunderlich
Great Plains Outfitters
Darryl Giesbrecht
Great White Holdings
Lloyd McMahon
Great White Holdings, Ltd.
Lloyd McMahon & Glenda
Biensch
Grist Haven Lodge
Tony M. Kossey
Grizzly Trail Guiding &
Outfitting
Leo Schmaus
Grosso Outfitting
Clayton & Hilda Grosso
Guinn Outfitters
Rick & Denise Guinn
Gundahoo River Outfitters
Art Thompson
Gypsy Lake Lodge
Jeff Dodds
Happy Hunters Guiding &
Outfitting
Willi Kratzmann
**Hebert's Guide Service**
**Joe & Doreen Hebert**
Hebert Guide Service
Doreen Hebert
High Country Vacations
Bazil Leonard & Susan
Feddema
Homeplace Ranch
Mac Makenny
Horseback Adventures Ltd.
Tom Vinson
J.W. & Edith Nagy Outfitting
J.W. & Edith Nagy
Jack Franklin Outfitting
JH Trail Rides
Del Whitford
Jim Fisher Guiding &
Outfitting
Jim Fisher
Jordy McAuley Outfitting
Jordy McAuley
K Country Outfitting
Keith Koebisch
Kevin Rolfe Outfitters
Kevin Rolfe
Kingfisher Drifting, Ltd.
Michael Truch
Kostynuk Outfitting
Sam Kostynuk
Lazy H Trail Co.
Richard & Connie Blair
Leonard Outfitting
Bazil Leonard
Lloyd Lake Lodge
Richard & Mary Jean Pliska
Lost Guide Outfitters
Gary Bracken
M & M Ranch
Neil & Becky Maclaine
Magnum Outfitters
Roy Thompson
Mawdsley Lake Lodge
Glen Coulter
McKenzie's Trails West
Ron McKenzie
McKenzie Brothers Outfitting

Bruce & Linda McKenzie
McMillan River Outfitters
Dave Coleman
Mike Zelman & Sons Guide
Service
Mike Zelman
N.W.T. Outfitters
Darrell & Duane Nelson
Nahanni Wilderness
Adventures. Ltd.
David Hibbard
North Alberta Outfitters
Troy & Lisa Foster
North Alberta Ventures
Dollard Dallaire
North Alta Ventures
Dollard & Shelly Dallaire
North River Outfitting
Ron Nemetchek
Northeast Alberta Wilderness
Outfitters, Inc.
Charles Graves
Northern Adventures
Pat Frederick
Northern Wilderness Outfitters
Weldon & Peter Prosser
Ongaro Outdoors
Outlaws Guiding & Outfitting
Frank Raymond
Pawistik Lodge
Scott Jeffrey
Percival Trophy Hunts
Doug Percival
Plihal Guiding & Outffiting
Gene Plihal
Poplar Ridge Outfitters, Inc.
Harvey McNalley
Porcupine Creek Outfitters
Brent Sinclair
Rams Head Outfitters
Stan Simpson
Ranch Country Outfitters
Perry McCormick
Raven Outfitters
Wayne Whitherspoon
Ray Cross & Sons Outfitting
Ray W. Cross
Redstone Trophy Hunts
David & Carol Dutchik
Ridge Country Outfitters
Bill Morton
Rocking Star Trail Rides
Willie Kadatz
Ron Loucks Outfitting
Ron Loucks
Ryk Visscher Bowhunting
Adventures
Ryk Visscher
Saddle Peak Trail Rides
Dave Richards
Sands & Miller Outfitting
Don Miller & Charlie Sands
Saracen Head Outfitter
Ed Regnier
Sheep Creek Outfitters
Frank Simpson
Sherwood Guides & Outfitters
Lois or Pete McMann
Silver Fox Outfitters
Eric Rauhanen
Silver Sage Outfitters
Billy Franklin
Silvertip Outfitters
Eric Grinnell
Skyline Trail Rides
Dave Flato
Smith & Overguard Outfitting
Jim Smith & Steve Overguard
South Paw Outfitters
Rene & Kelly Semple
South Ram Outfitters
Lorne Hindbo
South Ram Outfitters

Lorne & Sharmane Hindbo
**Stricker Outfitting, Ltd.**
Sunset Guiding & Outfitting
Duane D. Papke
Sven-Erik Jansson Associates
Sven-Erik Jansson
Tall Timbers Outfitting
David Sharp
Tamarack Hunting Enterprises
Justin Henry
Tazin Lake Lodge
Gordon Wilson
Team Whitetail Outfitting
Darcy Zelman
Timberline Tours
Paul Peyto
Todd Loewen Outfitting
Todd Loewen
**Tom Scott Outfitting**
**Tom Scott**
Trails Unlimited
Hank Peterson
Triple S Outfitting
Stuart & Ruby Sinclair-Smith
Trophy Quest Outfitters
Dean Regehr
Trophy Stalkers
Doug Olson
Tsayta Lake Lodge
Graham Perry
Twilight Guiding & Outfitting
Marcel Morin
Ukrainetz Guided Hunts
Mike Ukrainetz
Upper-Edge Outfitters
Rick Borysiuk
Vic Forchuk & Sons Outfitting & Guides
Vic Forchuk
Warner Guiding & Outfitting
Ron Warner
West Coast Safaris
Rod Hunter
Western Adventures
Glenn & Leslie Huber
**Western Guiding Service**
Whispering Hill Trophy Hunters & Outfitters
Jay Stewart
Whispering Pine Outfitters
Gordon & Lynn Utri
Whitetail Safaris
Paul Glen Carlson
Wild Rose Whitetails
Wilderness Ranch
Dick Hansen
Willow Lane Ranch
Keith & Leanne Lane
Wind Valley Guiding & Outfitting
Ken Fraser & Shelly Paul
Wingshooters Guiding Service Chris
Wolf-Creek Outfitters
Robert Irvine
Wolf Lake Wilderness Camp
Wolverman Wilderness Outfitters
Walchuk & Degenhardt & Slager

## British Columbia

Daryl Buchholtz
Dennis Gunn
Frank J. Hicks
Mark Irvine
Frank Methot

Steven J. Mohr
Fred Olson
Arnold Schwartz
Glen R. Drinkall
Gordon M. Elliott
Larry Loney
Mrs. Barbara Peden
Rudolf Waloszek
William Ashe
Denys Bell
Norman Blaney
Shawn Boot
Robert Jimmie
Wallace J. Paley
Allan B. Roberts
Michael Schneider
Brian Swift
Andy Cahoose
Harro Obst
Randy Saugstad
Karl Schmideder
Richard Solmonson
Theodore L. Williams
Wayne Zorn
Harry Chingee
Charlie Faessler
Alan Madley
Robert Milligan
Eberhard Mussfeld
Fred Peisl
Steve Smith
Jack Sylvester
Rush Dalziel
Don Smith
Kevan Bracewell
Alfred Joseph
Terry E. Cooke
Timothy Cushman
Dale Ethier
Richard Fahselt
Floyd Grinder
James Matarozzo
William C. Zimmer
Robert J. Cutts
Charlie Davidson
Lawrence Giesbrech
William Heaton, Sr.
Juergen Krebs
Herb Leake
Karl Oysmueller
Robert G. Paley
Frank Sill
Wayne N. Wiebe
Danny Cahoose
Keith B. Connors
Peter W. Grundmann
Stuart G. Maitland
Max & Viola Searls
Peter L. Bookmyer
David L. Burr
Ray Coldwell
Arthur Meldrum
Ralph Voll
Boyce J. Williams
Tom Nichol
Victor Sorensen
Thomas Christy
Douglas A. Davis
Tery Frank
Rolf Hussinger
Donald F. Letcher
John Reinhart
William Sorensen
James Vantine
Werner Burghardt
Walter Ernst
Scott R. Farr
Albin Hochsteiner
John R. Kettle
Wayne Louie
Gary &Terry Marcer & Grant Powell
Larry Sulin

Gerald Geraci
Dennis Hale
Amedee G. Isnardy
David Lougheed
Gary Lynn Moore
Tommy Timothy
Raymond J. Carry
Marvin Desjarlais
Lawrence Elkins
Leonard Ellis
Norman Grove
Jack E. Hamilton
Shelly Nicol
Thomas Reynolds
James E. Shockey
Mack Squinas
George Betemps
Ron Emmelkamp
Tony Petal
Ronald Price
**A/Z Outfitters**
**Bill DuBois**
Albert Cooper Guide & Outfitters
Albert Cooper
Alpine Ridge Guiding & Outfitting
Allan Strauss
Andy Hagberg Guiding
Andy Hagberg
April Point Lodge
Eric Peterson
Arctic Waterways/Whitewolf Adventure
Barry Beales
Ashnola Guide & Outfitter
Clarence Schneider
Ashnola Guide Outfitters
Clarence Schneider
Baldy Mountain Outfitters
Harry Leuenberger
Balm of Gilead Hunt Club
Rudy & Elsie Messaros
Bear Lake Guides & Outfitters
Dirk & Traute Schuirmann
Bear Paw Guide & Outfitters
Dennis & Irene Smith
Beaverfoot Lodge
Don Wolfenden
Bella Coola Outfitting Co., Ltd.
Leonard Ellis
Big Bar Guest Ranch
Big Bay Marina & Fishing Resort
Kay Knierim
Big Nine Outfitters
Barry Tompkins
Blaine R. Southwick Outfitting
Blaine Southwick
Blaine R. Southwick Outfitting, Ltd.
Blaine Southwick
Blunt Mountain Outfitters
Norm Blaney
Bogie Mtn./Besa River Outfitters
Pal Gillis
Bougie Mnt. Besa River Outfitting
Paul Gillis
Bowron River Guiding
Jack Pichette
Bracewell's Alpine Wilderness Adventures
Gerry Bracewell
Bradford & Co. Guide Services
Myles & Sherry Bradford
Bradford & Co. Guide Services, Ltd.
Myles Bradford
Campsall Outfitters
Hank Campsall
Canadian Adventure Safaris

Odd Aasland
Canadian Advenutre Safaris
Odd Aasland
Canadian River Expeditions
**Cariboo Mountain Outfitters**
**Bradley Bowden**
Cariboo West Outfitters
Gary & Peggy Zorn
Cassier Stone Outfitters
Dan Stobbe
Chilcotin River Guide Outfitter
William Mulvahill
Christina Falls Outfitters, Inc.
Darwin Watson
Churn Creek Outfitters
Eric Mikkelson
Coast Mountain Holidays
Roma Richburg
Coast Mountain Wilderness Lodge
Ralph Voll
Coastal Inlet Adventures
Collingwood Bros. Guides & Outfitters
Ray & Reg Collingwood
Collins Guiding
Darrel A. Collins
Columbia River Outfitters
Richard Hark
Copper River Ranch
Ben Ridennoure
Coyote Creek
Edward Cretney
Diamond M Outfitting
Terry Spriggs
Dick Blewett Outfitting
Dick Blewett
Eagle Crest Guide Outfitters
George Pedneault
Eagle River Guide Outfitting
Eric Havard
Eaglecrest Guide Outfitters
East Kootenay Outfitters
Joe Juozaitis
Edmund Lake Lodge
Herb & Anna Dyke
Elk Valley Bighorn Outfitters, Ltd.
Robert Fontana
Eureka Peak Lodge & Outfitters
Stuart Maitland
Fawnie Mt. Outfitters & Moose Lake Lodge
John Blackwell
Findlay Creek Outfitters
Eric Godlien
Finlay River Outfitters
Rick McLean
Folding Mountain Outfitters, Ltd.
Dale Drinkall
Fournier Bros. Outfitting
Greg Fournier
Fournier Brothers Outfitting
Greg Fournier
Frontier's Farwest
Debbie Patterson
Frontier Hunting
Doug Davis
G.F. Moore Enterprises
Gordon F. Moore
G.O.A.B.C.
Gana River Outfitters
Bill MacKenzie
Gemstar Outfitting
Brian Schuck
Glacier Peak Adventures, Inc.
Gary Koopman
Granby Guides & Outfitters
Barry Brandow
Great Canadian Ecoventures
Tom Faess

Grizzly Basin Outfitters
Wilfrid Boardman
Grizzly Lake Outfitters
Ron Fitch
Grizzly Outfitters
Phil Gillis
Gundahoo River Outfitters,
Inc.
Art Thompson
Hallett Lake Outfitters
Allen Ray
Hodson Guiding Services
D. Hodson
Horseshoe Creek Outfitters,
Ltd.
Ray Jackson
Icha & Illgatcho Mountain
Outfitters
Roger Williams
Icha & Illgatcho Mountains
Outfitters
Roger Williams
Indian River Ranch Guides &
Outfitters
Jamie Schumacher
Inzana Outfitters
Terry Stocks
Itcha Mountain Outfitters
B.H. Fraser
Kasba Lake Lodge
Kawdy Outfitters
Stan Lancaster
Kazchek Lake
Harm Wernicke
Kettle River Guides &
Outfitters
Melvin Kilback
Kiniskan Outfitters
Bruce Creyke
Kluachesi Lake Outfitting
Kluane Wilderness Lodge
Klukas Lake Ranch
Glen Kilgour
Kyllo Brothers
Ken Kyllo
Kyllo Brothers
Ken & Scott & Peter Kyllo
Lakes District Hunting Lodge
Hans-Joerg Hartl
Lamoureux Outfitters
Martin Lamoureux
Larry Erickson's Alpine
Outfitters
Larry Erickson
Layton Bryson Outfitting &
Trail Riding
Layton Bryson
Lehman Creek Outfitters
Dave Altherr
Liard River Outfitters
Mike Belfour
**Love Bros. & Lee Ltd.**
**Ron Fleming & Brenda Nelson**
Lower Kootenay Guide
Outfitters, Ltd.
Don Bullock
M. Mulvahill Hunting
Mike Mulvahill
M.C. Outfitting
Chuck Christensen
Mackenzie Mountain
Outfitters
Stan Stevens
McCowan's Sporting
Adventures
Harry McCowan
McKay Brothers Guides &
Outfitters
Bernard & Patrick McKay
Middle River Hunting &
Fishing
Martin Grainger
Monashee Outfitting

Volker Scherm
Monroe Cattle Co.
Mike Monroe
Moose Lake Lodge
**Moose Valley Outfitters**
**Ronald Steffey**
Mooseskin Johnny Lake
Outfitters
Don McIntyre
Morice River Outfitting
John Shepert
Muncho Lake Outfitters
Arnold Henhapl
Muskwa Safaris
Garry & Sandra Vince
Nahanni Butte Outfitters
Greg Williams
Nanika Guiding
Jim Tourond
Nass Headwaters Guiding &
Outfitting
Ken Belford
Nicola Outfitters
Dan Stobbe
Nimmo Bay Resort
Craig Murray
Nisutlin Bay Outfitters
Philip Smith
Niut Trails Outfitting
Eric Hatch
North Coast Adventures, Inc.
Wayne Price
North Country Jet Boat
Charters
Northern Woodsman
Outfitting
Les Allen
Northwest Big Game Outfitters
Jack Goodwin
Northwest Ranching &
Outfitting
Heidi Gutfrucht
Norwest Guiding & Outfitting
Jeff Beckley
Okanagan Outfitters
Marc & Marcella Hubbard
Omineca Guide & Outfitters
Herb Badey
One Eye Outfit
Mike McDonough
Opatcho Lake Guide &
Outfitters
Ralph Maida
Ottertail River Outfitting
Alan & Mary Young
Painter's Lodge
Harley Elias
Palliser River Guides &
Outfitters
Cody Tegart
Palliser River Outfitters
Gordon Burns
Parrot Mountain Outfitters
Miles Fuller
Peace Country Wilderness
Adventures
Horst Mindermann
Peaceful Valley Wilderness
Outfitters
Len Pickering
Pine River Ventures
Dale & Andy Copeland
Pink Mountain Outfitters
Klaur Knocke
Pitka Mountain Outfitters, Ltd.
Colonel R. Anderson
Purcell Wilderness Guiding &
Outfitting
Gary Hansen
Purcell Wilderness Guiding &
Outfitting
Gary E. Hansen
Quesnel Lake Wilderness

Adventures
Ken Davis
Rainbow Mountain Outfitting
David Dorsey
Ram Creek Outfitters
Steven Leuenberger
Rocky Mountain Adventures
Gordon Jeck
Rocky Mountain High Outfitter
& Guides
Barry Scott
Rocky Mountain Lodge, Ltd.
Henry Fercho
Rocky Mountain Outfitter, Ltd.
Rocky Mountain Outfitters
Carmen Dempsey
Ross Peck Outfitters
Ross Peck
Sage Creek Outfitters
Darrel Winser
Sailcone Wilderness Fishing
Salmon King Lodge
Lucie Drovin
Salmon River Outfitters
Dwayne Nikkels
Schuk Outfitting
Doug Schuk
Scoop Lake Outfitters, Ltd.
Darwin Cary
Scoop Lake Outfitters
Darwin Cary
Selkirk Big Game Outfitters
Phil Desmazes
Sentinel Mountain Ent.
Dave Drolet & Roy Pattison
Shesley River Outfitters
Rudy Day
Sidka Tours
Sikanni River Outfitters
Doug Percival
Silent Mountain Outfitters
Dieter Bohrmann
Smoke Mountain Guiding
John Mould
Sonora Resort
Alan Moss
Spring King Charters, Ltd.
Ray & Ellen Hepting
Spruce Lake Outfitting
Bryan Buchanan
Steam Boat Mountain
Outfitters
Stein River Outfitters
Leo & Doris Ouellet
Steiner Bros. Guide &
Outfitting
Ray Steiner
Stelkia Ranch
Aaron Stelkia
Stone Mountain Safaris
Dave & Ellie Wiens
Stuart-Trembleur Outfitters
William Stanton
Sugar Valley Outfitters
Bernie Jaeger
Suskeena Lodge
Floyd Boyd
Tahltan Outfitters
Fletcher Day
Taku Safari
Guy Anttila
Tatlatui Wilderness
Bob Henderson
Tetsa River Outfitters
Cliff Andrews
The Blackwater Company
Ron Thompson
The Dolphins Resort
Clint Cameron
Thunder Mountain Outfitters
Larry Bartlett
Tincup Wilderness Lodge
Larry Nagy

Toby Creek Outfitters
Lloyd Harvey
Trembling Pines Outfitter
Roy Mulvahill
Trophy West Guide Outfitters
Donald Rose
Tsuniah Lake Lodge
Eric Brebner
Tsylos Park Lodge &
Adventures
Lloyd McLean
Tukii Lodge
Dave Hooper
Turnagain River Outfitters
Eugene Egeler
Tweedsmuir Park Guides &
Outfitters
Bob Nielsen
Uncha Mountain Outfitters
Stefan Muehlmeyer
Upper Stikine River
Adventures, Ltd.
Jerry Geraci
Vaseux Creek Outfitters
Jim Wiens
Vaseux Lake Lodge
Peter & Denise Axhorn
Wayne Mueller Guide &
Outfitters
Wayne Mueller
Webb Outfitting
Fred A. Webb
West Coast Outfitting
Bob Welsh
West Kettle Outfitters, Ltd.
Peter Grosch
Whatshan Guides & Outfitters
Ken Robins
Wistaria Guiding
Gary Blackwell
Wolverine Mountain Outfitters
Tim Chushman
Yohetta Wilderness
Adventures, Ltd.
Goetz Schuerholz

# SASKATCHEWAN

24 North Outfitters
Phil Chalifour
40 Mile Coulee Farm
Albert & Martha Hicks
A & E Outfitters
A.R.M. Outfitters
Aerial Adventures
Barry & Lana Prall
All-Terrain Outfitters
Marlon Parasiuk
All-The-Way-Holloway
Outfitters
Angler's Trail Resort
Ivan & Elsie Fauth
Antonichuk Outfitters
Willard Antonichuk
Athabasca Camps
Cliff Blackmur
Athabasca Fishing Lodges
Cliff Blackmu
Athabasca Lone Wolf Camps
Brian MacDonald
Austin's Service
Austin Tide
B & L Cabins & Outfitters Ltd.
Blaine & Linda Cunningham
Bait-Masters Hunting Camps
Brain E. & Sylvia Hoffart
Barrier Beach Resort
Scott O'Bertos
Barrier Chaparral Lodge

George & Kasandra O'Bertos
Bay Resort
Bear Claw Outfitters
Bear Creek Outfitters
Beaver Lodge Fly-Inn Ltd.
Wallace & Elaine Johnson
Besnard Lake Lodge
Beyond La Ronge Lodge
Andy & Beatrice Fecke
Big Eddy Camp
Solomon Carriere
Big Foot Outfitters
Dave & Ethel Flannigan
Big Island Cove Resort
Big Sandy Resort
Calvin & Annie Wingert
Black Bear Island Lake Lodge
Earl Mockellky
Black Bear Outfitter
Bloomfield's Ballantyne Bay
Resort
George & Fran Bloomfield
Boreal Camp Services
Morton G. Harbicht
Briarhill Boar Outfitters
Zandra Slater
Bronson Lake Outfitters
Buck & Bear Wilderness
Adventures
Buckhorn Bay Resort Outfitters
Lee & Sylvia Donison
Bucks, Bulls, and Bears
Buckskin Joe Outfitting
Camp Grayling
Margy Michel & Ed White
Camp Kinisoo Ltd
Christopher and Sheila Brown
Campeau Guiding & Outfitting
Alvin J. Campeau
Can-Am Outfitters Ltd.
Chris or Cindy Shea
**Careen Lake Lodge**
**Jack & Eileen O'Brien**
Caribou Creek Lodge Ltd.
Dwight & Bev Whitley
Carrieres Camp
Freda & John V. Carriere
Carrot Lake Outfitters
Charlie Brown's Outfitting &
Guiding Service
Churchill River Voyageur
Lodge
Terry Helary
Churchill River Wilderness
Camps
Klaas & Norman Knot
Circle Lakes Angus
Clarke Lake Lodge/Clearwater
Adv.
Clearwater Raft Tours
Copeau Creek Outfitters
David Osecki
Country Flavor
Don & Linda Kirby
Cracking River Guides
Al Fiddler
Craig's Pasquia Hills Vacation
Farm
Dorothy & Osborne Craig
Craig's Place - Outfitters
Dorothy & Craig Osborne
Cree River Lodge
Cree River Lodge Ltd.
eter Evaschesen
Crystal Lodge
John Midgett
Cuelenaere Lake Lodge
Larry Cherneski
Cumberland House Outfitters
Ltd.
Cup Lake Fishing Camp
Lindsay & Barry Brucks
CutArm Outfitters

D & D Camps Ltd.
Dick Cossette
Dahl Creek Outfitting
Darsana Lodge
Carl & Marg Boychuk
Davin Lake Lodge
Wes Borowsky
Deception Lake Lodge
Delaronde Resort
Deschambault Lake Resort
Twylla Newton
Dillon Lake Outfitting
Arsene Nezcroche
Dobbin Lake Lodges
N. Silzer & J. Motoshosky
Dore Lake Lodge
Alex & Vicky Shukin
Eastview Wilderness Ranch
Corrina Gray & Larry Kapeller
Elks Hills Holiday Ranch
Leo & Erna Oestreicher
Elusive Saskatchewan
Whitetail Outfitter
Harvey McDonald
Ena Lake Lodge
A. Shane MacKinnon
English River First Nations
Resort
Alfred Dawatsare
Flotten Lake Resort
Abram & Paula Rempel
Forsyth Ranch
Ian & Irene Forsyth
Foster Lake Lodge
Trent Brunanski
G & S Marina Outfitters
Robert Schulz & Peter Gallo
G W Outfitting
Garry Walters
Gary Simon Outfitting/
Thunder Rapids Lodge
Ghost Ranch Outfitting
Paul Chartrand
Glen Hill's Trophy Expeditions
Glen Hill
Goose Creek Outfitters
John Zwack
**Granger's Cheemo Lodge**
Grayling Lodge
C. Veikle & R. Brackenbury
Green Lake Lodge
Karen & Bob Henderson
Greenwater & Marean Lake
Outfitting
Grey Owl Camp Fly-In Ltd.
Tom Schuck & Dick Panter
Hasbala Lake Lodge
Hatchet Lake Lodge
George Fleming
Hawkrock Outfitters
Allan Serhan
Hepburn Lake Lodge
Dennis Callbeck
Heritage Outfitters
Ralph D. Holowaty
Hillcrest Motel & Outfitters
Kelly & Debra Morrell
Hilliard's Pine Island Camp
Butch & Neva Hilliard
Horse Creek Vacation Farm
Ruby Elford
J R Outfitters
Jim's Camp - Nistowiak Falls
James Daniel McKenzie
John Fonos Outfitting
Johnson's Resort
Paul
Johnson River Camp
Jean Graham
Josdal Camps
Tyrone Josdal
K & P Outfitters
S. Van Buskirk & S. Garrett

K Bar T Vacation Ranch
Keith & Eleanor Taylor
Katche Kamp Outfitters
Bill & Jeanne Blackmon
Kee Kamps Ltd
Dean Orosz or Barry Elton
Keeley Lake Lodge
Gary & Gloria Callihoo
Kelan Suffold Vacation Farm
Ken & Lana Webster
Kenyon Lake Fly-In
Kevin Tourand Outfitting
Kutawag Lake Outfitter
La Ronge Eagle Point Resort
Lac La Peche Resort
Eloise Vigeant
Lakeland Marine Rentals Ltd.
Albin Walcer
Lakeview Inn
Wilbur George Bauer
Lamplighter Lodge
Roy & Cynthia Petrowicz
Lindwood Lodge
Gerry Lindskog
Little Bear Lake Resort
Dwayne Giles
Little Pine Lodge
Wendy & Pat Tyson
Lone Spruce Outfitters
Steven & Nancy Butler
Long's 4 Seasons Resort Ltd.
Gary Long
Longview Farm
Bob & Charlene Siemens
Lucky Lake Outfitters
Willard Ylioja
M & M Outfitters
Moe Morley
M & N Resort
Wayne Chepil
Macoun Lake Island Lodge
Harvey Nelson & Rodgeer
Herman
MacSwaney's Cabins
Magee's Farm
Beatrice & Tom Magee
Mann Lake Outfitters
Larry K Stoudt
Maple Grove Resort
Martin's Cabins
Denis & Betty Martin
Martineau River Outfitters
Medicine Rapids Resort
Larry Stevenson
Medinski's Outfitting Services
Larry Medynski
Mel-Sask Outfitters
Mercer Outfitting
Ken & Pat Auckland
Michel Lodge
Wayne & Kathy Berumen
Ministikwan Lodge
Dave Werner
Minor Bay Camps
Gerald & Paulette Howard
Minowukaw Lodge and Joe's
Cabins
Lu Crawford
Mista Nosayew Outfitters
Jeff Janzen
Mistatim Outfitting
Mistik Lodge
Gary Carriere
Moen's Riverside Lodge
Moose Horn Lodge
Marvin Peterson
Moose Range Lodge
Mystic Magic Wilderness
Lodge
Nagle Lake Outfitters
Bob & Stella Rodwin
Newmart Fishing Resort
Bob Humen & Mauthe

Niska Hunting & Fishing Camp
Nordic Lodge
Donna Carlson
Norseman Outfitters
D. Rutherford & A. Kjerstad
North Haven Lodge
Jim & Gail Marple
Northern Cross Resort Ltd.
Jeff Jesske & Co.
Northern Echo Lodge
Jim or Carol Eberle
Northern Lights Lodge Ltd.
Ted & Diana Ohlsen
**Northern Nights Outfitters,**
**Ltd. - Bruce & Brian Basken**
Northern Reflection Lodge
Eddy Jones
Northern Sask Wilderness
Hunts
Keith Heisler
Oliver Lake Wilderness Camp
Michel Dube
ON TARGET Guiding &
Outfitting
Dan Dunn
Orban's Outfitting
Darrell Orban
Otter Basin Outfitters
Don & Beverly Gillespie
Otter Creek Outfitters
Ronald & Geraldine Lavoie
Overflow River Outfitters
Gerald Melnychuk
Overland Cross Country Lodge
Wayne & Diane Elliott
Pardoe Lake Lodge
Vern Hunt
Paull River Wilderness Camp
Wayne Galloway
Pelican Narrows U-Fly-In Ltd.
Ray Fournier
Pickerel Bay Cabins
Ray or Gail Twedt
Pickerel Point Concessions
Pickerel Point General Store
Cliff & Susan Maruk
Pierce Lake Lodge
Pierceland Outfitters
Zane Pikowicz
Pine Cove Resort
Pine Grove Resort
Margaret Lucyshyn
Pipe Stone Guiding
Pipestone Lake Lodge Ltd.
Marvin Bather
Pleasant Vista Farm
George & Doris Husband
Pointer Lake Fishing Lodge
Bryce Liddell
Prairie Outfitters
Potter & Westin & Slabik
Prairie Sun Outfitting
Shawn Prestupa
Prairieland Outfitters
Don Anderson
Preferred Habitat
Management
Pruden's Point Resort
R & R Wilderness Lodge
R. Jenson & R. Reylonds
R P Outfitters
Rabbit Creek Outfitters
Allan Folden
Rainbow Lodge
Rick & Ricky Lawrence
Red's Camps
Ron MacKay
Redwillow Outfitting
Larry & Angela Schmitt
Riel Bosse Outfitting &
Guiding
Riverside Service & Cabins
Ron Anderson

RLR Outfitter
Richard Rydeik
Rocky Lake Cabins
Duane & Glenda Bohlken
Russell's Churchill River
Camps
Jim Russell
Safari River Outdoors
Barry Samson
Sask Can Outfitters
Bonace Korchinski
Schmidt's Outdoor
Expeditions
Schwab Simmentals
David & Janet Schwab
Scott Lake Lodge
Ken & Suzanne Gangler
Selwyn Lake Lodge
Gord/Mary Daigneault-
Wallace
Shadd Lake Cabins
Nancy McKay
Silver Tip Outfitting
Garry & Zay Debienne
Simoneau's Outfitting
Simpson's Sportsman's Lodge
Sisip (Duck) Outfitting Camp
Robert McKay
Skull Lodge
Slim's Cabins
Jim & Veronica Woods
South Bay Cabins & Services
Percy Depper
Spring Valley Guest Ranch
Jim Saville
Springwater Outfitters
Spruceville Outfitters
Brian Washburn
Squaw Creek Outfitters
Sturgeon Landing Outfitters
T & D Amisk Cabins
Tawaw Cabins
Emil & Merrel Berg & K. Wolffe
The New Canoe West Resort
Harold Breault
The Stopping Place
Deb & Ian McLeod & Family
Thistlethwaite Outfitting
Thompson's Camps, Inc.
Garry Thompson
Thompson Lake Lodge/Triple
Lake Camps
Mike Chursinoff
Thunderbird Camps
Thunderhill Outfitter
Timberline Outfitting
Bernard or Harvey Nokinsky
Tobin Lake Resort
Connie Anklovitch
Toby's Trophy Treks
Toby Coleman
Top Gun Outfitters
Reg Bousquet
Torch Valley Country Retreats
George & Jean Lidster
Tower Lodge
Trails End Outfitters
Rolie Morris
Triveet Lake Fly-In
Stuart Warrener
True North Lodge
Turtle Lake Lodge
Maurice & Jeanette Blais
Twin Bay Resort Ltd.
Ken & Naomie Selb
Twin Marine
Curtis Lockwood
Two Fingers Fishing Camp
Two Spirit Guest Ranch &
Retreat
Lee Cryer & Denise Needham
Upland Outfitting Services
Vermillion Lake Camp

W J Wilderness Camp
James Custer
Wadin Bay Resort
Wayne Buckle & Audrey Miller
Wagons Roll Inn
Lorraine & Ray Ostrom
Wally's Place
Gen Assailly & Wally Nicklin
Waterhen Lake Store & Resort
Whiskey Jack Camp
White Fox Hotel Outfitting
Robert Shatula
White Gull River Outfitters
Tom McLane
White Swan Lake Resort
Gerry Wenschlag
Whitetails Only
David Fountain
Wild Man Outfitters/Poplar
Point Resort
Wild Thing Outfitters
Tim Fehr
Wild Wings Outfitters
R. Ross & B. Carter R. Button
Wilson's Lodge
Windy Acres Vacation Farm
Elliot & Reta Kimpton
Wounded Knee
Dick & Judy Wells
Wright's Vacation Farm
Ken & Linda Wright


# YUKON TERRITORIES

Edward G. Dolhan
Arctic Red River Outfitters,
Ltd.
Kelly & Heather Hougen
Babala Stone Sheep Outfitters
Ltd.
Jim Babala
Barney's Fishing & Tours
Blackstone Safaris
Lee Bolster
**Bonnet Plume Outfitters, Ltd.**
**Charlie Stricker**
Campfire Adventures
Canadian Wilderness Travel
Ltd.
**Canoe North Adventures**
Cassiar Mountain Outfitters
Kirby Funnell
Cedar & Canvas Adventures
Circle VH Outdoor Adventures
Cloudberry Adventures Ltd.
Dalton Trail Lodge
David Young Outfitters Ltd
Devilhole Outfitters
Dickson Outfitters Ltd.
David Dickson
Ecole Otter Wilderness
Ecosummer Yukon
Expeditions
Faro Yukon Fishing Tours
Heart Bar Ranch
Horizons North Ltd.
Inconnu Lodge
Kanoe People Ltd.
Jerry Anderson
Klondike River Rafting
Kluane Outfitters Ltd.
Ross Elliott
Koser's Yukon Outback
Koser Outfitters
Pete Koser
Kruda Che Wilderness Guiding
Ron
Kusawa Outfitters
Klaas Heynen

MacMillan River Outfitters
Dave Coleman
Macmillan River Tours
Nahanni-NWT Safaris
Rick Furniss
**Nahanni Wilderness**
Nahanni River Adventures Ltd.
Oldsquaw Lodge
Otter Falls Wilderness
Adventure
Pack Trails North Adventures
Paul's Fishing Tours - North of
60
Peacock's Yukon Camps Ltd.
Peter Jensen Guide & Outfitter
Pete Jensen
Prospect Yukon Wilderness &
Watercraft
Rainy Hollow Wilderness
Adventures Ltd.
Rogue River Outfitters
Cliff Hanna
Ruby Range
Keith & Debbie Carreau
Ruby Range Wilderness Lodge
Sifton Wilderness Adventures
Snowy Mountain Safaris
Stan Reynolds Outfitting, Ltd.
Stan Reynolds
Sunshine Valley Guest Ranch
Takhini River Guiding
Tatshenshini Expediting Ltd.
Taylor's Place Fishing Camp
Teslin Outfitters
Terry Wilkinson
Teslin Outfitters
Doug Smarch
The Hitching Post
Trophy Stone Safaris, Ltd.
Curt Thompson
Wanderlust Wilderness
Adventures
Widrig Outfitters, Ltd.
Chris Widrig
Wilderness Fishing Adventures
Russ Rose & Sheri Lockwood
Wind River Wilderness Tours
Wolf Adventure Tours
Yukon Hunting & Guiding Ltd.
Rod Hardie
Yukon Outfitters' Association
Stan Reynolds
Yukon Outfitting
Yukon Tours

# Colorado

## State and Federal Agencies

Colorado Agencies of Outfitters Registry
1560 Broadway, Suite 1340
Denver, CO  80202
phone: (303) 894-7778

Colorado Dept. of Natural Resources
1313 Sherman, Room 718
Denver, CO  80203
phone: (303) 866-3311

Forest Service, Rocky Mountain Region
740 Simms Street
Lakewood, CO 80225
phone: (303) 275-5350
TTY: (303) 275-5367

Bureau of Land Management
Colorado State Office
2850 Youngfield St.
Lakewood, Co. 80215-7093
phone: (303) 239-3600
fax: (303) 239-3933
Tdd: (303) 239-3635
Email:  msowa@co.blm.gov

## National Parks

Mesa Verde National Park, CO 81330
phone: (303) 529-4465

Rocky Mountain National Park
phone: (303) 586-2371

## License and Report Requirements

• State requires licensing of Outdoor Professionals.
• State requires an "Inter-Office Copy of Contract with Client" be submitted each time a client goes with an Outfitter.  Colorado Agencies of Outfitters Registry sends this copy to client to fill out and return to their agency.

## Associations, Publications, etc.

Colorado Outfitters Association
PO Box 1304
Parker, CO  80134
phone: (303) 841-7760

International Hunter Education Assoc.
PO Box 347
Jamestown, CO  80455
phone: (303) 449-0631
fax: (303) 449-0576

Federation of Fly Fishers
http://www.fedflyfishers.org

CO Bass Chapter Federation
2713 Garden Drive
Ft. Collins, CO 80526
phone: (303) 221-3608

Colorado Whitewater Association
2 Silver Cloud
Boulder, CO  80302
phone: (303) 447-0068
fax: (303) 776-4068

Colorado Whitewater Association
PO Box 4315
Englewood, CO  80155-4315
phone: (303) 430-4853

Colorado Dude & Guest Ranch Assoc.
PO Box 300
Tabernash, CO  80478
phone: (970) 887-3128
directory: (970) 887-9248
fax: (970) 887-2456

The Dude Ranchers' Association
PO Box F-471
LaPorte, CO  80535
phone: (970) 223-8440
fax: (970) 223-0201

DudeRanches.com
http://www.duderanches.com

# Useful information for the state of
# Idaho

## State and Federal Agencies

Outfitter & Guides Licensing Board
1365 N. Orchard, Room 172
Boise, ID 83706
phone: (208) 327-7380
fax: (208) 327-7382

Idaho Fish & Game Dept.
600 South Walnut
Boise, ID 83707
phone: (208) 334-3700

Forest Service
Northern Region
Federal Bldg.
PO Box 7669
Missoula, MT 59807-7669
phone: (406) 329-3616
TTY: (406) 329-3510

Clearwater National Forest
phone: (208) 476-4541

Idaho Panhandle, Coeur d'Alene-
Kaniksu-St. Joe National Forests
phone / TTY: (208) 765-7223

Nez Perce National Forest
phone: (208) 983-1950

Bureau of Land Management
Idaho State Office
1387 S. Vinnell Way
Boise, ID 83709-1657
phone: (208) 373-3896
or  (208) 373-plus ext.
fax: (208) 373-3899

Office Hours 7:45 a.m. - 4:15 p.m.

## Associations, Publications, etc.

Idaho Outfitters & Guides Association
PO Box 95
Boise, ID 83701
phone: (208) 342-1438

Trout Unlimited Idaho Council
3845 Whiskey Jack Road
Sandpoint, ID 83864-9466
phone: (208) 263-6937
fax: (208) 265-2996

American Fisheries Society
1525 Kathleen
Coeur d'Alene, ID 83814
phone: (208) 769-1414

Federation of Fly Fishers
http://www.fedflyfishers.org

Idaho Bass Chapter Federation
8012 W. Arapaho Ct.
Boise, ID 83703
phone: (208) 853-9039

Paddler Magazine
PO Box 1341
Eagle, ID 83616
phone: (208) 939-4500
fax: (208) 939-4600

daho Guest and Dude Ranch Assoc.
HC 72
Cascade, ID 83611
phone: (208) 382-4336
message phone: (208) 382-3217

DudeRanches.com
http://www.duderanches.com

## License and Report Requirements
• State requires licensing of Outdoor Professionals.
• State requires that every Outfitters be it bird, fish, big game, river rafting, trail riding or packing file a "Use Report" annually.
• Currently, no requirements for Guest/Dude Ranches.

# Montana

## State and Federal Agencies

Montana Board of Outfitters
Dept. of Commerce
Arcade Building - 111 North Jackson
Helena, MT  59620-0407
phone: (406) 444-3738

Montana Dept. of Fish, Wildlife & Parks
1420 East 6th
Helena, MT  59620
phone: (406) 444-2535

Forest Service, Northern Region
Federal Building
PO Box 7669
Missoula, MT 59807-7669
phone: (406) 329-3616
TTY: (406) 329-3510

Bureau of Land Management
Montana State Office
P.O. Box 36800
Billings, Montana 59107-6800
phone: (406) 255-2885
fax: (406) 255-2762
Email - mtinfo@mt.blm.gov
Office Hours: 8:00 a.m. - 4:30 p.m.

## National Parks

Glacier National Park
phone: (406) 888-5441

## License and Report Requirements

- State requires licensing of Outdoor Professionals.
- State requires an "Annual Client Report Log" for all Hunting and Fishing Outfitters.
- State does not regulate River Guides.
- Guest/Dude Ranches need to get an Outfitter license only if they take guest to fish or hunt on land that they do not own.

## Associations, Publications, etc.

Montana Outfitters & Guides Assoc.
PO Box 1248
Helena, MT  59604
phone: (406) 449-3578

Rocky Mountain Elk Foundation
PO Box 8249
Missoula, MT 59807-8249
phone: (406) 523-4500
fax: (406) 523-4550

North America Gamebird Association
1214 Brooks Avenue
Raleigh, NC  27607
email: gamebird@naga.org

Fishing Outfitters Assoc. of Montana
Box 311
Gallatin Gateway, MT  59730
phone: (406) 763-5436

Federation of Fly Fishers
PO Box 1595
502 South 19th, Ste. #1
Bozeman, MT  59771
phone: (406) 585-7592
fax: (406) 585-7596
http://www.fedflyfishers.org

Montana Bass Chapter Federation
12345 O'Keefe Road
Missoula, MT 59812
phone: (406) 728-8842

Flathead Whitewater Association, Inc.
PO Box 114
Whitefish, MT  59937
phone: (406) 862-2386

Montana Big Sky Ranch Association
1627 West Main Street, Suite 434
Bozeman, MT  59715

DudeRanches.com
http://www.duderanches.com

# New Mexico

## State and Federal Agencies

New Mexico Game & Fish Dept.
Villagra Building
Santa Fe, NM 87503
phone: (505) 827-7975

Forest Service
Southwestern Region
517 Gold Avenue SW
Albuquerque, NM 87102
phone: (505) 842-3300
TTY: (505) 842-3898

Carson National Forest
phone: (505) 758-6200

Cibola National Forest
phone/TTY: (505) 761-4650

Gila National Forest
phone: (505) 388-8201

Lincoln National Forest
phone: (505) 434-7200

Santa Fe National Forest
phone: (505) 438-7840

Bureau of Land Management
New Mexico State Office
1474 Rodeo Road
Santa Fe, NM 87505
P.O. Box 27115
Santa Fe, NM 87502-0115
Information Number: (505) 438-7400
fax: (505) 438-7435
Public Lands Information Center (PLIC):
(505) 438-7542
Office Hours: 7:45 a.m. - 4:30 p.m.

## National Parks

Carlsbad Caverns National Park
3225 National Parks Hwy.
Carlsbad, NM 88220
phone: (505) 785-2232

## License and Report Requirements

• State requires that Hunting Outfitters be licensed.
• State requires the filing of an "Annual Report of Outfitters' Clients" for hunting only.
• "Use Permit" required for Fish and River Outfitters using BLM and Forest Service lands. They are not required to file any reports.

## Associations, Publications, etc.

New Mexico Council of Outfitters & Guides, Inc.
160 Washington SE #75
Albuquerque, NM 87108
phone: (505) 764-2670

American Fisheries Society
PO Box 30003, Dept. 4901
Las Cruces, NM 88003
phone: (505) 521-7279

Federation of Fly Fishers
http://www.fedflyfishers.org

Trout Unlimited Rio Grande Chapter
9307 Galaxia Way, NE,
Albequerque, NM 87111
phone: (505) 243-1336

New Mexico Bass Chapter Federation
PO Box 717
Socorro, NM 87801
phone: (505) 835-1200

DudeRanches.com
http://www.duderanches.com

Useful information for the state of

# Utah

## State and Federal Agencies

Utah Dept. of Natural Resources
1636 W. North Temple
Salt Lake City, UT 84116
phone: (801) 538-4700

Forest Service
Intermountain Region
324 25th Street
Ogden, UT 84401-2310
phone: (801) 625-5306
TTY: (801) 625-5307

Bureau of Land Management
Utah State Office
324 South State Street, Suite 301
P.O. Box 45155
Salt Lake City, Utah 84145-0155
Information Number: (801) 539-4001
fax: (801) 539-4013
Office Hours: 8:00 a.m. - 4:00 p.m.

## National Parks

Arches National Park
Moab, UT 84532
phone: (801) 259-8161

Bryce Canyon National Park
Bryce Canyon, UT 84717
phone: (801) 834-5322

Canyonlands National Park
1Moab, UT 84532
phone: (801) 259-3911

Capitol Reef National Park
Torrey, UT 84775
phone: (801) 425-3791

Zion National Park
Springdale, UT 84767
phone: (801) 772-3256

## License and Report Requirements

- State does not license or register Outfitters, Guides, Captains or Lodges.
- State Parks & Recreation Division requires that River Rafting Guides and Outfitters register and file a "River Outfitting Company Registration".
- BLM, Forest Service and National Park Service require a "Use Permit" and "User Fee" for Boating, Fish and River Outfitters using their lands. Guides and Outfitters required to file a "Year End Report of Activities".

## Associations, Publications, etc.

Trout Unlimited Rio Grande Chapter
9307 Galaxia Way, NE,
Albequerque, NM 87111
phone: (505) 243-1336

Federation of Fly Fishers
http://www.fedflyfishers.org

New Mexico Bass Chapter Federation
PO Box 717
Socorro, NM 87801
phone: (505) 835-1200

World Wide Outfitter & Guide Assoc.
PO Box 520400
Salt Lake City, UT 84152-0400
phone: (801) 566-2662

# Wyoming

## State and Federal Agencies

Wyoming Dept. of Commerce
Board of Outfitters
1750 Westland Rd.
Cheyenne, WY 82002
phone: (800) 264-0981
phone: (307) 777-5323
fax:(307) 777-6715

Wyoming Game & Fish Dept.
5400 Bishop Blvd.
Cheyenne, WY 82002
phone: (307) 777-4601

Forest Service
Intermountain Region
324 25th Street
Ogden, UT 84401-2310
phone: (801) 625-5306
TTY: (801) 625-5307

Bridger-Teton National Forests
phone: (307) 739-5500

Bureau of Land Management
Wyoming State Office
P.O. Box 1828
Cheyenne, WY 82003
phone: (307) 775-6BLM or 6256
fax: (307) 775-6082
Office Hours: 7:45 a.m. - 4:30 p.m.

## National Parks

Grand Teton National Park
phone: (307) 739-3610

Yellowstone National Park
phone: (307) 344-7381

## Associations, Publications, etc.

Wyoming Outfitters & Guides Assoc.
PO Box 2284
239 Yellowstone Ave., Suite C
Cody, WY 82414
phone: (307) 527-7453
fax: (307) 587-8633

Jackson Hole Outfitters & Guide Association
850 W. Broadway
Jackson Hole, WY 83001
phone: (307) 734-9025

Trout Unlimited Wyoming
PO Box 1022
Jackson, WY 83001
phone: (307) 733-1530

Federation of Fly Fishers
http://www.fedflyfishers.org

Wyoming Bass Chapter Federation
106 Folsom Drive
Rock Springs, WY 82901
phone: (307) 382-4742

DudeRanches.com
http://www.duderanches.com

Jackson Hole Chamber of Commerce
PO Box E
Jackson Hole, WY 83001
phone: (307) 733-3316
jhchamber@sisna.com

## License and Report Requirements
• State requires licensing of Outdoor Professionals.
• State requires that Big Game Outfitters file a "Year-End Report".
• Fishing Outfitters need to get a permit to fish on BLM land.
• Outfitters and Guest/Dude Ranches must file a "Use" or "Day Report" with the Wyoming Forest Service if they Fish, Hunt or Raft on Forest Service Land.

# Useful information for the provinces of
# Canada

## Alberta:
### Ministries and Agencies

Dept. of Environmental Protection
9945-108 Street
Edmonton, Alberta, Canada T5K 2C6
phone: (403) 427-8636
fax: (403) 422-6339
email: Lfunke@env.gov.ab.ca

Natural Resources Service
9945-108 Street
Edmonton, Alberta, Canada T5K 2C6
phone: (403) 427-6749

### Associations, Publications, etc.

Alberta Outfitters Association
Box 277
Caroline, Alberta, Canada T0K 0M0
phone/fax: (403) 722-2692

Professional Outfitters Assoc. of
Alberta
PO Box 67012 Meadowlark Park
Edmonton, Alberta, Canada T5R 5Y3
phone: (403) 486-3050
fax: (403) 484-4942

The Alberta Fish & Game Association
6924-104 Street
Edmonton, Alberta, Canada T6H 2L7
phone: (403) 437-2342
fax: (403) 438-6872

Ducks Unlimited Canada
#202, 10470-176 Street
Edmonton, Alberta, Canada T5S 1L3
phone: (403) 489-2002

North America Gamebird Association
1214 Brooks Avenue
Raleigh, NC 27607
email: gamebird@naga.org

## British Columbia:
### Ministries and Agencies

Department of Fisheries & Oceans
200 Kent Street
Ottawa, Ontario Canada K1A 036

Ministry of the Environment
810 Blanshard St., 4th Floor
Victoria, B.C. Canada V8V 1X4
phone: (604) 387-9422

Ministry of Business, Tourism & Culture
1117 Wharf St.
Victoria, B.C. Canada V8V 2Z2
phone: (604) 387-1683

### Associations, Publications, etc.

Guide Outfitters Association of British
Columbia
PO Box 94675
Richmond, B.C. Canada V6Y 4A4

Federation of Fly Fishers
http://www.fedflyfishers.org

## Saskatchewan:
### Ministries and Agencies

Saskatchewan Environment And Resource Management
3211 Albert St.
Regina, SK Canada S4S 5W6

### Associations, Publications, etc.

Federation of Fly Fishers
http://www.fedflyfishers.org

## Yukon Territories:
### Ministries and Agencies

Dept.of Renewable Resources
Box 2703
Whitehorse, Y.T. Canada 71A 2C6
phone: (403) 667-5460

### Associations, Publications, etc.

Yukon Fish & Game Association
PO Box 4434
Whitehorse, Y.T. Canada Y1A 3T5
phone: (403) 667-2843

Yukon Outfitters Association
Box 4548
Whitehorse, Y.T. Canada Y1A 2R8
phone: (403) 668-4118

Picked-By-You Questionnaire
# Top Guided Flyfishing

Name of your Field Guide:_____
(Person that guided you in the field)

Date of Trip_____Location_____  Day trip ☐      Overnight trip ☐

Was this a Family Trip where your children were actively involved in the activities?   Yes ☐    No ☐

**Technique used:** _____

**Species caught or observed:** _____

Catch ☐          Catch and Release ☐

|  | OUTSTANDING | EXCELLENT | GOOD | ACCEPTABLE | POOR/INFERIOR | UNACCEPTABLE |
|---|---|---|---|---|---|---|
| 1. How helpful was the Outfitter (Guide, Captain or Lodge) with travel arrangements, fishing regulations, permits etc.?......................................... | ☐ | ☐ | ☐ | ☐ | ☐ | ☐ |
| 2. How well did the Outfitter (Guide, Captain or Lodge) provide important details that better prepared you for your fishing trip (clothing, equipment, information on the fish and the water, list of "take along", etc.)?................. | ☐ | ☐ | ☐ | ☐ | ☐ | ☐ |
| 3. How would you rate the Outfitter's (Guide, Captain or Lodge) office skills in handling deposits, charges, reservations, returning calls before and after your trip?....................................................................................... | ☐ | ☐ | ☐ | ☐ | ☐ | ☐ |
| 4. How would you rate the accommodations (tent, cabin, lodge, etc.)?............ | ☐ | ☐ | ☐ | ☐ | ☐ | ☐ |
| 5. How would you rate the equipment provided by the Outfitter (Guide, Captain or Lodge) during your trip (boats, tackle, rods, airplanes, etc.)?...... | ☐ | ☐ | ☐ | ☐ | ☐ | ☐ |
| 6. How would you rate the cooking (quantity, quality and cleanliness of the service)?...................................................................................................... | ☐ | ☐ | ☐ | ☐ | ☐ | ☐ |
| 7. How would you rate your Guide's Attitude — Politeness — Disposition?..... | ☐ | ☐ | ☐ | ☐ | ☐ | ☐ |
| 8. How would you rate your Guide's knowledge of the area?........................... | ☐ | ☐ | ☐ | ☐ | ☐ | ☐ |
| 9. How would you rate your Guide's knowledge of the fish (feeding cycle, habits, type of flies to be used, etc.)?............................................................ | ☐ | ☐ | ☐ | ☐ | ☐ | ☐ |
| 10. How were your fish prepared for trophy mounting and/or for the trip home? (For Catch and Release write N/A)............................................................. | ☐ | ☐ | ☐ | ☐ | ☐ | ☐ |

|  | OUTSTANDING | EXCELLENT | GOOD | ACCEPTABLE | POOR/INFERIOR | UNACCEPTABLE |
|---|---|---|---|---|---|---|

11. How would you rate the skills and the attitude of the Staff overall?............ ☐ ☐ ☐ ☐ ☐ ☐

12. How would you rate the quality of the waters?.......................................... ☐ ☐ ☐ ☐ ☐ ☐

13. How would you rate the quality of the fish?............................................... ☐ ☐ ☐ ☐ ☐ ☐

14. How would you rate the flexibility of your Guide or Captain to meet your goal(s) ?............................................................................................... ☐ ☐ ☐ ☐ ☐ ☐

15. How would you rate the overall quality of your fishing experience?........... ☐ ☐ ☐ ☐ ☐ ☐

|  | GOOD | FAIR | POOR |
|---|---|---|---|

16. How would you describe the weather conditions?.................................... ☐ ☐ ☐

17. Did the Outfitter (Guide, Captain or Lodge) accurately represent the overall quality of your experience (quality of waters, fish, accommodations, etc.)?...................................................................................... ☐ YES   ☐ No

18. Did you provide the Outfitter (Guide, Captain or Lodge) with truthful statements regarding your personal needs, your skills and your expectations?...................................................................................... ☐ YES   ☐ No

19. Would you use this Outdoor Professional/Business again?........................ ☐ YES   ☐ No

20. Would you recommend this Outdoor Professional/Business to others?..... ☐ YES   ☐ No

Comments: _____
_____
_____
_____
_____
_____
_____
_____
_____
_____
_____
_____
_____
_____
_____
_____
_____
_____

Will you permit Picked-By-You to use your name and comments in our book(s)? ☐ YES   ☐ No

Signature_____

**Note**: This is an example of one of the Questionnaires used in the Picked-By-You surveyes. Each one of the activites (Big Game Hunting, Freshwater Fishing, Saltwater Fishing, etc.) utilized a specifically tailored questionnaire.

# Index of Outdoor Professionals by Activity

## Top Rated
## Big Game Hunting

4 + 2 T Ranch
A/Z Outfitters Ltd
Arrowhead Outfitters
Beaver Creek Outfiters
Big Rack Adventures
Bonnet Plume Outfitters
Boulder Lake Lodge
Buckhorn Ranch Outfitters
Cariboo Mountain Outfitters
Castle Creek Outfitters
Cecil Ralston Guide & Outfitters
Chase Hill Outfitters
Cow Creek Outfitters
Darby Mountain Outfitters
Darwin Ranch
Double J Outfitters
Echo Canyon Guest Ranch & Outfitters
Elk Creek Outfitters
Esper's Under Wild Skies
EW Watson & Sons Outfitting
Flat Iron Outfitting
Frazier Outfitting
Garvey Brothers Outfitters
Grand & Sierra Outfitters
Greer Outfitters
Hebert's Guide Service
Hidden Basin Outfitters
Hidden Hollow Hideaway
Horse Creek Outfitters
JM Bar Outfitting
John Henry Lee Outfitters
K Bar Z Guest Ranch & Outfitters
Kibler Outfitting
Lakeview Resort & Outfitters–Co
only(no Mt)
Lightning Creek Ranch
Lone Tom Outfitting
Lone Tree Outfitting & Guide Service
Love Bros & Lee Outfitters
Mitchell Outfitting
Moose Valley Outfitters
P Cross Bar Ranch
Phil's Bowhunting Adventures
Pusch Ridge Outfitters
Ramshorn OutfittersRed Desert
Adventures

Renshaw Outfitting, Inc.
R.L. Sourbrine Outfitters & Sons
S & W Outfitters
Samuelson Outfitters
San Juan Outfitting
Rick Wemple Outfitting
River S Enterprises
Spadafora Ranch Lodge
Stricker Outfitting Ltd.
Swift Creek Outfitters
T Lazy T Outfitters
Terrero General Store & Riding Stables
Timberline Outfitters
Tom Scott Outfitting
Triangle C Ranch
Twin Pine Ranch
Western Guiding Services
Western Wyoming Trophy Hunts
White Tail Ranch/WTR Outfitters, Inc.
Wild West Outfitters

## Top Rated
## Bird Hunting

Eagle Nest Lodge
Echo Canyon Outfitters
Good's Bird Hunt/Eagle Outfitters
Triple B Outfitters
Wapiti River Guides
Western Guiding Service

# Index of Outdoor Professionals by Activity

## Top Rated
## Fly Fishing

Alpine Anglers Fly Shop & Boulder Mtn.Advs.
Broken Arrow Ranch
Dragonfly Anglers
Eagle Nest Lodge
East Slope Anglers
Esper's Under Wild Skies
Grossenbacher Guides
Hatch Finders
Heise Expeditions
John Henry Lee Outfitters
Love Bros & Lee Outfitters
Mike Wilson's High Mountain Drifters, Inc.
Rocky Fork Guide Service
Solitude River Trips
The Complete Fly Fisher
The Reel Life
The Reflective Angler
The Troutfitter
Tite Line Fishing

## Top Rated
## Outdoor Wilderness Adventures

WSRT / "Birds of Prey" Expeditions

## Top Rated
## River Adventures

Bill Dvorak's Kayak and Rafting Expeditions
Canoe North Adventures
Headwaters River company
Idaho Afloat
Mild to Wild Rafting
Nahanni Wilderness Adventures
Northwest Voyageurs
Rocky Mountain River Tours, Inc.
Sheri Griffith Expeditions
Solitude River Trips
Wapiti River Guides
Warren River Guides
Western Waters and Woods
Whitewater Voyageurs
Wild Rockies Tours

## Top Rated
## Freshwater Fishing

Careen Lake Lodge
Flat Iron Outfitting
Granger's Cheemo Lodge
Northern Nights
Wapiti River Guides
Western Waters and Woods

# Index of Outdoor Professionals by Activity

## Top Rated Western Adventures

Beaver Meadow Resort Ranch
Boulder Lake Lodge
Broken Arrow Ranch
Cheff Guest Ranch
Darby Mountain Outfitters
Darwin Ranch
Double Spear Ranch
Early Guest Ranch
Echo Canyon Guest Ranch
Esper's Under Wild Skies
EW Watson & Sons Outfitting
Frazier Outfitting
Granite Creek Guest Ranch
Hargrave Cattle & Guest Ranch
Hartley Guest Ranch
Hidden Hollow Hideaway
Iron Wheel Ranch
John Henry Lee Outfitters
K Bar Z Guest Ranch & Outfitters
Lakeview Resort & Outfitters
Lozier's Box "R" Ranch
Maynard Ranch
Monture Face Outfitters
Nine Quarter Circle Ranch
Rich Ranch, LLC
San Juan Outfitting
Schmittel Packing & Outfitting
Skyline Guest Ranch
White Tail Ranch/WTR Outfitters, Inc.

# Index of Outdoor Professionals by State/Province

# Index of Outdoor Professionals by State/Province

# Index of Outdoor Professionals by State/Province

# Index of Outdoor Professionals by State/Province

# Alphabetical Index by Company Name

# Alphabetical Index by Company Name

# Alphabetical Index by Company Name

PBY - Top Rated Rocky Mountain Adventures